Phalaenopsis

The Genus in Pictures

Wesley Higgins and Peggy Alrich

Phalaenopsis: the Genus in Pictures

Wesley Higgins and Peggy Alrich

International Phalaenopsis Alliance
182 Guinea Road
Stamford, CT 06903 USA

ISBN-13: 978-0-692-37391-0
ISBN-10: 0-6923-7391-8

Library of Congress Control Number: 2015902467
Printed in Taiwan, V-Gold Printing Co., LTD
First Printing: March 2015

Introduction

The genus *Phalaenopsis* currently consists of 72 species divided into four subgenera and six sections. Within Orchidaceæ, *Phalaenopsis* is a member of subfamily *Epidendroideæ*, tribe *Vandeæ* and subtribe *Aeridinæ*.

This genus is comprised of mostly epiphytic and some lithophytic or terrestrial species that are natives of India, southern to eastern China, southern Japan, Taiwan, Southeast Asia (Myanmar to Vietnam, Malaysia, Indonesia & the Philippines), New Guinea and northeastern Australia (Queensland).

The plants are monopodial with succulent leaves on short stems. The inflorescence, rising off the stem from among the leaves, can have a few to hundreds of showy, variously-colored flowers that have a distinct trilobed lip.

With the publication of *Genera Orchidacearum* (6: 233), the genus *Phalaenopsis* now includes these former genera: *Doritis, Hygrochilus, Kingidium, Lesliea, Nothodoritis, Ornithochilus* and *Sedirea*.

P·H·A·L·A·E·N·O·P·S·I·S CLASSIFICATION

Subgenus *Phalaenopsis*

Section *Phalaenopsis* Bentham

Type Species: *P. amabilis* - (Linnaeus) Blume

P. amabilis - (Linnaeus) Blume
P. aphrodite - Reichenbach f.
P. celebensis - H.R. Sweet
P. equestris - (Schauer) Reichenbach f.
P. lindenii - Loher
P. philippinensis - Golamco ex Fowlie & C.Z. Tang
P. sanderiana - Reichenbach f.
P. schilleriana - Reichenbach f.
P. stuartiana - Reichenbach f.

Section *Polychilos* (Breda) Reichenbach f.

Type Species: *P. cornu-cervi* - (Breda) Blume & Reichenbach f.

P. amboinensis - J.J. Smith
P. bastianii - O. Gruss & Röllke
P. bellina - (Reichenbach f.) Christenson
P. cochlearis - Holttum
P. corningiana - Reichenbach f.
P. cornu-cervi - (Breda) Blume & Reichenbach f.
P. doweryensis - Garay & Christenson
P. fasciata - Reichenbach f.
P. fimbriata - J.J. Smith
P. floresensis - Fowlie
P. fuscata - Reichenbach f.
P. gigantea - J.J. Smith
P. hieroglyphica - (Reichenbach f.) H.R. Sweet
P. inscriptiosinensis - Fowlie
P. javanica - J.J. Smith
P. kunstleri - Hooker f.
P. lueddemanniana - Reichenbach f.
P. maculata - Reichenbach f.
P. mannii - Reichenbach f.
P. mariae - Burbidge ex Warner & Williams
P. mentawaiensis - O. Gruss
P. micholitzii - Rolfe
P. modesta - J.J. Smith
P. pallens - (Lindley) Reichenbach f.
P. pantherina - Reichenbach f.
P. pulchra - (Reichenbach f.) H.R. Sweet
P. reichenbachiana - Reichenbach f. & Sander
P. robinsonii - J.J. Smith
P. rundumensis - P.J. Cribb & A. Lamb
*P. speciosa** - Reichenbach f.
P. sumatrana - Korthals & Reichenbach f.
*P. tetraspis** - Reichenbach f.
P. venosa - P.S. Shim & Fowlie
P. violacea - Witte
P. viridis - J.J. Smith

Subgenus *Parishianæ* (H.R. Sweet) Christenson

Section *Parishianæ* H.R. Sweet

Type Species: *P. parishii*- Reichenbach f.

P. appendiculata - C.E. Carr
P. gibbosa - H.R. Sweet
P. lobbii - (Reichenbach f.) H.R. Sweet
P. malipoensis - Z.J. Liu & S.C. Chen
P. parishii - Reichenbach f.
P. thailandica - O. Gruss & Röth

Section *Esmeralda* Reichenbach f.

Type Species: *P. pulcherrima* - (Lindley) J.J. Smith

P. buyssoniana - Reichenbach f.
P. pulcherrima - (Lindley) J.J. Smith
P. regnieriana - Reichenbach f.
P. ubonensis - O. Gruss

Section *Deliciosæ* Christenson

Type Species: *P. deliciosa* - Reichenbach f.

P. chibae - T. Yukawa
P. deliciosa - Reichenbach f.
P. finleyi - Christenson
P. mirabilis - (Seidenfaden) Schuiteman
P. mysorensis - Saldanha

Section *Aphyllæ* H.R. Sweet

Type Species: *P. stobartiana* - Reichenbach f.

P. honghenensis - F.Y. Liu
P. lowii - Reichenbach f.
P. natmataungensis - (T. Yukawa, Nob. Tanaka & J. Murata) Dalström & Ormerod
P. stobartiana - Reichenbach f.
P. taenialis - (Rchb. f.) Christenson & Pradhan
P. wilsonii - Rolfe
P. zhejiangensis - (Z.H. Tsi) Schuiteman

**Phalaenopsis speciosa* is most likely a synonym of *P. tetrapsis.*

Subgenus ***Ornithochilus*** (Lindley) Kocyan & Schuiteman

Type Species: *P. difformis* - (Wallich ex Lindley) Kocyan & Schuiteman

P. cacharensis - (Barbhuiya, B.K. Dutta & Schuiteman) Kocyan & Schuiteman

P. difformis - (Wallich ex Lindley) Kocyan & Schuiteman

P. yingjiangensis - (Z.H. Tsi) Kocyan & Schuiteman

Subgenus ***Hygrochilus*** (Pfitzer) Kocyan & Schuiteman

Type Species: *P. marriotiana* - (Reichenbach f.) Kocyan & Schuiteman

P. japonica - (Rchb.f.) Kocyan & Schuiteman

P. marriottiana - (Rchb.f.) Kocyan & Schuiteman

This species is called *P. marriottiana*, because the name *P. parishii* had already been taken.

P. subparishii - (Z.H. Tsi) Kocyan & Schuiteman

Phalaenopsis amabilis, Rumphia **4**: 194 (1848)

THE
Species

Phalaenopsis amabilis △

◁ *Phalaenopsis amabilis*

(Linnaeus) Blume

Bijdragen tot de Flora van Nederlandsch Indie, 7: 294 (1825).

SUBGENUS: *Phalaenopsis*,
SECTION: *Phalaenopsis*

Phalaenopsis amabilis is the type species of the genus. This vandaceous genus is comprised of 72, mostly epiphytic (some lithophytic or terrestrial), species spread throughout most of Asia, from eastern India to the Philippines, then Korea to northern Australia. These monopodial plants have large succulent, drooping leaves with short stems, giving rise to an inflorescence which can have a few to hundreds of flowers each with a distinct trilobed, clawed lip.

Habitat: A medium sized epiphyte usually occurring at elevations up to 600 meters in rain forests; growing on tree trunks and branches overhanging rivers, swamps and along streambeds.

Culture: Easy; warm-hot, moderate light.
Temperature: 18-30°C • ***Humidity:*** 70-85%

Flowers: 6-10cm; Spring through Summer; faintly or not fragrant.
Longevity: 45-60 days. •
Inflorescence: 40-60cm; arching to pendent.

Distribution: Indonesia, the Philippines and New Guinea to north-eastern Australia (Queensland).

▽ *Phalaenopsis amabilis*

Phalaenopsis amboinensis

J.J. Smith, *Bulletin de Département de l'Agriculture aux Indes Néerlandaises, Buitenzorg*, **45**: 23 (1911).

SUBGENUS: *Phalaenopsis*, SECTION: *Polychilos*

This species is often confused with *P. sumatrana* which has dense trichomes on the apex of the midlobe, and densely packed papillae in the posterior callus, these are not found in *P. amboinensis.*

Habitat: A small sized epiphyte growing on tree trunks away from direct sunlight at low elevation, 80 meters, in shady, humid forests with year round rainfall.

Culture: Easy; hot, shade. ***Temperature:*** 23-33°C ● ***Humidity:*** 70-85%

Flowers: 4-7.5cm; Late Winter-early Spring, very fragrant.
Longevity: 20-30 days ● *Inflorescence:* 15-20cm; arching; often branched.

Distribution: Indonesia (Ambon Island to Sulawesi) and Papua New Guinea

Phalaenopsis aphrodite

Reichenbach f., *Hamburger Garten-Blumenzeitung*, **18**: 35 (1862).

SUBGENUS: *Phalaenopsis*, SECTION: *Phalaenopsis*

The species is often confused with *P. amabilis* but differs with its red lip disc, a triangular midlobe and smaller flowers.

itat: Medium sized epiphyte growing mainly in open forest on high :rees in primary and secondary forests at elevations of 0-300 meters.

Culture: Easy; warm-hot, moderate light.
Temperature: 20-32°C ● ***Humidity:*** 70-85%

Flowers: 6.5-9cm; Winter-Spring, faintly to not fragrant.
gevity: 30-50 days. ● ***Inflorescence:*** 50–80cm; arching to pendent racemes.

Distribution: southern Taiwan to the southwestern Philippines (Sulu Archipelago)

Phalaenopsis amboinensis

△ *Phalaenopsis aphrodite* ▽

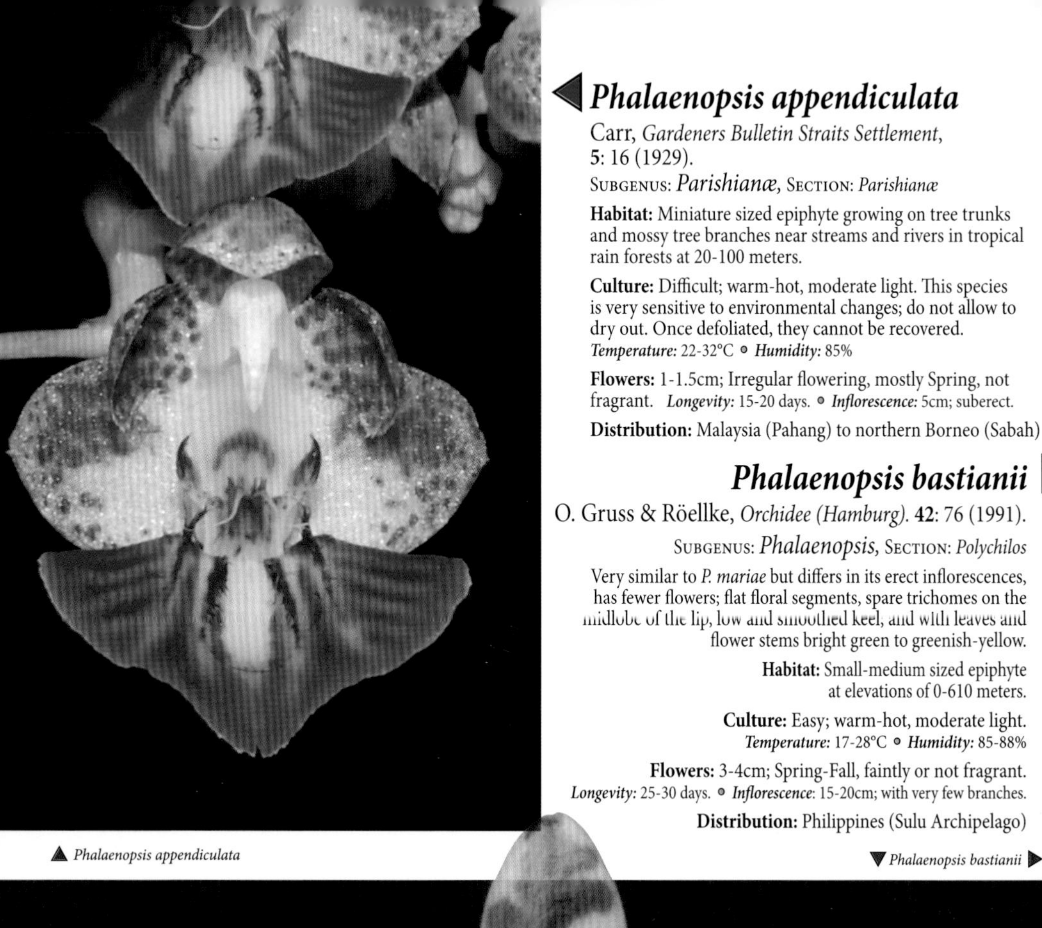

Phalaenopsis appendiculata

Carr, *Gardeners Bulletin Straits Settlement*, **5**: 16 (1929).

Subgenus: *Parishianæ*, Section: *Parishianæ*

Habitat: Miniature sized epiphyte growing on tree trunks and mossy tree branches near streams and rivers in tropical rain forests at 20-100 meters.

Culture: Difficult; warm-hot, moderate light. This species is very sensitive to environmental changes; do not allow to dry out. Once defoliated, they cannot be recovered. ***Temperature:*** 22-32°C ◦ ***Humidity:*** 85%

Flowers: 1-1.5cm; Irregular flowering, mostly Spring, not fragrant. ***Longevity:*** 15-20 days. ◦ ***Inflorescence:*** 5cm; suberect.

Distribution: Malaysia (Pahang) to northern Borneo (Sabah)

Phalaenopsis bastianii

O. Gruss & Röellke, *Orchidee (Hamburg)*. **42**: 76 (1991).

Subgenus: *Phalaenopsis*, Section: *Polychilos*

Very similar to *P. mariae* but differs in its erect inflorescences, has fewer flowers; flat floral segments, spare trichomes on the midlobe of the lip, low and smoothed keel, and with leaves and flower stems bright green to greenish-yellow.

Habitat: Small-medium sized epiphyte at elevations of 0-610 meters.

Culture: Easy; warm-hot, moderate light. ***Temperature:*** 17-28°C ◦ ***Humidity:*** 85-88%

Flowers: 3-4cm; Spring-Fall, faintly or not fragrant. ***Longevity:*** 25-30 days. ◦ ***Inflorescence:*** 15-20cm; with very few branches.

Distribution: Philippines (Sulu Archipelago)

▲ *Phalaenopsis appendiculata*

▼ *Phalaenopsis bastianii* ▶

Phalaenopsis bellina

(Rchb.f.) Christenson, *Brittonia*, **47**: 58 (1995).

Subgenus: *Phalaenopsis*, Section: *Polychilos*

The leaves are thicker, more succulent and pendent than those of *P. violacea*.

Habitat: Epiphytes on tall trees in the canopy layer at elevations of 0-200 meters. The upper canopy has relatively low moisture with definite dry and wet cycles when compared to the riverside.

Culture: Easy; warm-hot, moderate light.
Temperature: 23-33°C ◦ ***Humidity:*** 80%

Flowers: 5-6cm; Summer-Fall, very fragrant.
Longevity: 25-30 days. ◦ ***Inflorescence:*** 8-10cm; zigzag. The plants can reflower year after year, so do not cut off green, viable inflorescences.

Distribution: eastern Indonesia (Borneo)

Phalaenopsis buyssoniana ▶

Reichenbach f., *Gardeners' Chronicle*, **1888**(2): 295 (1888).

Subgenus: *Phalaenopsis*, Section: *Esmeralda*

P. buyssoniana has 76 chromosomes instead of the typical 38.

Habitat: Terrestrial plants found growing in the lowland forests with many rigid roots laid out around the stem, at elevation of 0-900 meters.

Culture: Easy; intermediate, moderate to strong light.
Temperature: 16-27°C ◦ ***Humidity:*** 60%+

Flowers: 39.5cm; Summer-Fall, not fragrant.
Longevity: 15-19 days. ◦ ***Inflorescence:*** Up to 1 meter, erect.

Distribution: Thailand and Vietnam

▲ *Phalaenopsis buyssoniana*

halaenopsis bellina ▼

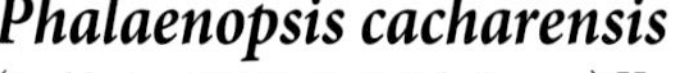

▲ *Phalaenopsis cacharensis*

▽ *Phalaenopsis celebensis*

▲ *Phalaenopsis cacharensis*

(Barbhuiya, B.K. Dutta & Schuiteman) Kocyan & Schuiteman, *Phytotaxa,* **161**(1): 67 (2014).

Subgenus: *Ornithochilus*

Habitat: Grows on the trees, whose bark is used as a fish poison. Usually found in wet, evergreen, lowland rain forests at 130 meters.

Culture: Unknown.
Temperature: 9-36°C ◦ ***Humidity:*** 87%

Flowers: 1.7cm; Summer-early Fall, fragrance unknown.
Longevity: unreported. ◦ ***Inflorescence:*** 35-38cm; racemose, branched.

Distribution: northeastern India (Assam)

Phalaenopsis celebensis ▷

H.R. Sweet, *Genera Phalaenopsis,* 66 (1980).

Subgenus: *Phalaenopsis,* Section: *Phalaenopsis*

Habitat: Epiphyte at elevations of 400-600 meters.

Culture: Easy; warm, low light.
Temperature: 23-30°C ◦ ***Humidity:*** 72-80%

Flowers: 3.0-3.5cm; Summer, faintly to not fragrant.
Longevity: 20-25 days. ◦
Inflorescence: 50-60cm; arched or pendent.

Distribution: eastern Indonesia (Sulawesi - Celebes)

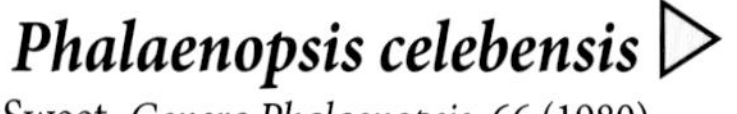

◀ *Phalaenopsis chibae*

T. Yukawa, *Annals of the Tsukuba Botanical Garden*, **15**: 19 (1996).

Subgenus: *Parishianæ*, Section: *Deliciosæ*

Habitat: Natural forms are found in tropical, moist forests in the vicinity of Da Lat, at elevations of 400-600 meters.

Culture: Easy; hot-warm, moderate light.
Temperature: 17-32°C ◦ ***Humidity:*** 70-80%

Flowers: 1.2cm; Spring, not fragrant.
Longevity: 15-20 days. ◦ ***Inflorescence:*** 11cm; erect, racemose.

Distribution: southern Vietnam

Phalaenopsis cochlearis ▷

Holttum, *Orchid Review*, **73**: 409 (1964).

Subgenus: *Phalaenopsis*, Section: *Polychilos*

Habitat: Epiphytes found in limestone forests at elevations of 500-700 meters.

Culture: Slightly difficult; warm, moderate light.
Temperature: 15-28°C ◦ ***Humidity:*** 80%

Flowers: 4-5cm; Spring-Summer, not fragrant.
Longevity: 20-25 days. ◦ ***Inflorescence:*** 30-51cm; suberect, branched.

Distribution: Malaysia to eastern Indonesia (Borneo)

Phalaenopsis chibae ▼

△ *Phalaenopsis cochlearis*

◀ *Phalaenopsis corningiana*

Reichenbach f., *Gardeners' Chronicle, n.s.*, **11**: 620 (1879).

Subgenus: *Phalaenopsis,* Section: *Polychilos*

Habitat: Found in mossy trees on limestone cliffs near waterfalls, at elevations between 450-600 meters.

Culture: Difficult; warm, moderate light.
Temperature: 25-30°C ◦ *Humidity:* 80%

Flowers: 5-6.25cm; Summer, very fragrant.
Longevity: 25-30 days. ◦ *Inflorescence:* 30cm; zigzag.

Distribution: eastern Indonesia (Borneo - Sarawak)

Phalaenopsis cornu-cervi ▶

(Breda) Blume & Reichenbach f., *Hamburger Garten- Blumenzeitung,* **16**: 116 (1860).

Subgenus: *Phalaenopsis,* Section: *Polychilos*

Habitat: Epiphyte or lithophyte in exposed lowland locations on stunted vegetation or high up in the canopy of dense riverine forests at elevations of 200-1,000 meters.

Culture: Easy; hot-warm, bright light.
Temperature: 15-32°C ◦ *Humidity:* 60-80%

Flowers: 3-5cm; Spring-Autumn, slightly fragrant.
Longevity: 15-25 days. ◦ *Inflorescence:* 9-42cm; racemose or paniculate, rachis persists and reflowers over many years.

Distribution: Myanmar to Vietnam, Malaysia, eastern India (Nicobar Islands) and Indonesia to the Philippines

◀ *Phalaenopsis corningiana*

▲ *Phalaenopsis cornu-cervi* ▼

◁ *Phalaenopsis deliciosa*

Reichenbach f., *Bonplandia (Hannover),* **2**: 93 (1854).

SUBGENUS: *Parishianæ,* SECTION: *Deliciosæ*

Habitat: Usually found above 300 meters in Borneo, and 600 meters or less in Thailand.

Culture: Easy; warm, moderate-strong light.
Temperature: 27-30°C ∘ *Humidity:* 80%

Flowers: 1.2-1.5cm; Summer-Fall, faintly to not fragrant.
Longevity: 7-12 days. ∘ *Inflorescence:* 20-25cm; arched, branched.

Distribution: southern China (Yunnan) India, Sri Lanka, Nepal, Myanmar to Vietnam, Malaysia and Indonesia to the Philippines

Phalaenopsis difformis

(Wallrich ex Lindley) Kocyan & Schuiteman, *Phytotaxa,* **161**(1): 67 (2014).

SUBGENUS: *Ornithochilus*

Habitat: Found on mossy branches of old gnarled tree trunks, in open humid, mossy, mixed and coniferous forests or at forest margins in the Himalayas, at elevations of 300-2,100 meters.

Culture: Easy; cool-intermediate, moderate light.
Temperature: 11-31°C ∘ *Humidity:* 45-95%

Flowers: 8mm-1.5cm; Summer, not fragrant.
Longevity: 20-25 days. ∘ *Inflorescence:* Up to 45cm; arching to pendulous

Distribution: southern China (Yunnan), northern India, Nepal, Myanmar to Vietnam and Malaysia to Indonesia

△ *Phalaenopsis deliciosa*

▼ *Phalaenopsis difformis*

Phalaenopsis doweryensis

Garay & Christenson, *Phalaenopsis,* 115 (2001).

Subgenus: *Phalaenopsis,* Section: *Polychilos*

Habitat: An epiphyte found in eastern Malaysia (Sabah), without a precise locality, at elevations of 0-150 meters.

Culture: Difficult; warm-hot, moderate-bright light.
Temperature: 23-32°C ◦ *Humidity:* 80-98%

Flowers: 4.5-5cm; Spring, slightly fragrant.
Longevity: 15-20 days. ◦ ***Inflorescence:*** 20cm; erect, racemose.

Distribution: far eastern Malaysia (northern Borneo - Sabah)

Phalaenopsis equestris

(Schauer) Reichenbach f., *Linnaea,* **22**: 864 (1850).

Subgenus: *Phalaenopsis,* Section: *Phalaenopsis*

Habitat: Epiphytes, found near streams in hot to warm valleys at elevations of 0-300 meters.

Culture: Easy; hot, moderate-bright light.
Temperature: 23-32°C ◦ ***Humidity:*** 70%

Flowers: 1.5-3cm; Spring, faintly or not fragrant.
Longevity: 15-25 days. ◦ ***Inflorescence:*** 30cm; racemose or paniculate.

Distribution: southern Taiwan (Hsiao & Lan Yü) to the Philippines

△ *Phalaenopsis equestris*

Phalaenopsis doweryensis ▽

◀ *Phalaenopsis fasciata*

Reichenbach f., *Gardeners' Chronicle, n.s.,* **18**: 134 (1882).

Subgenus: *Phalaenopsis,* Section: *Polychilos*

Habitat: Epiphytes on trees in the rain forest at elevations of 500 meters.

Culture: Easy; warm, moderate light.
Temperature: 24-32C ◦ *Humidity:* 70-80%

Flowers: 4.5-5cm; Summer-Autumn, weakly fragrant.
Longevity: 25-35 days. ◦ *Inflorescence:* 25 cm; suberect to curved, racemose, zigzag. The inflorescence can continue to reflower for years.

Distribution: the Philippines

Phalaenopsis fimbriata ▷

J.J. Smith, *Bulletin de Département de l'Agriculture aux Indes Néerlandaises, Buitenzorg,* ser. 3, **3**: 300 (1921).

Subgenus: *Phalaenopsis,* Section: *Polychilos*

Habitat: In moss and on trees in areas of high humidity around riversides, in hill forests and along limestone cliffs at elevations of 790-1,300 meters.

Culture: Easy; hot-warm, moderate light.
Temperature: 20-30°C ◦ *Humidity:* 80%.

Flowers: 2.5-5cm; end of Summer-Autumn, strongly fragrant.
Longevity: 25-30 days. ◦ *Inflorescence:* 27cm; racemose or paniculate.

Distribution: western Indonesia (Java, Sumatra and Sarawak)

▲ *Phalaenopsis fasciata*

▽ *Phalaenopsis fimbriata* ▷

◁ *Phalaenopsis finleyi*

Christenson, *Richardiana,* **11**: 80 (2011).

Subgenus: *Parishianæ,* Section: *Deliciosæ*

Habitat: Found in moist tropical forests at elevations of 0-160 meters.

Culture: Easy; warm-hot, moderate light.
Temperature: 10-35°C ◦ *Humidity:* 60%

Flowers: 1.5-2.0 cm; Early Summer-late Spring, not fragrant.
Longevity: 15-20 days. ◦ *Inflorescence:* 7-8cm; pendent.

Distribution: Myanmar, Thailand and Vietnam

Phalaenopsis floresensis ▷

Fowlie, *Orchid Digest,* **57**: 36 (1993).

Subgenus: *Phalaenopsis,* Section: *Polychilos*

Habitat: Found in areas of high temperature and high humidity, surrounding waterfalls or riversides in the lowlands at elevations of 150-300 meters.

Culture: Easy; hot, moderate light.
Temperature: 23-33°C ◦ *Humidity:* 72-84%

Flowers: 3.5-4cm; Spring-Summer, strongly fragrant.
Longevity: 20-25 days. ◦ *Inflorescence:* 18-20 cm; erect.

Distribution: eastern Indonesia (Lesser Sunda Islands - Flores)

Phalaenopsis finelyi

△ *Phalaenopsis floresensis* ▽

◀ Phalaenopsis fuscata

Reichenbach f., *Gardeners' Chronicle, n.s.,* **2**: 6 (1874).

Subgenus: *Phalaenopsis,* Section: *Polychilos*

Very similar to *P. kunstleri,* but differs mainly in having a longer column.

Habitat: Epiphytic, shady lowland to hill forests, from elevations of 0-1,000 meters, on trees near streams.

Culture: Easy; hot-warm, moderate light.
Temperature: 23-32°C ∘ *Humidity:* 70-82%

Flowers: 3.5-5cm; Summer (not particular), not fragrant.
Longevity: 20-25 days. ∘ *Inflorescence:* 50-60cm; racemose or paniculate.

Distribution: Malaysia, eastern Indonesia (Sumatra, Boreno) and the Philippines

Phalaenopsis gibbosa ▷

H.R. Sweet, *American Orchid Society Bulletin,* **39**: 1095 (1970).

Subgenus: *Parishianæ,* Section: *Parishianæ*

Habitat: Found in bright open forest of broad-leafed, evergreen forests at elevations of 500 meters.

Culture: Easy; hot-warm, moderate light.
Temperature: 17-32°C ∘ *Humidity:* 70-80%

Flowers: 1.5cm; Late Winter-early Spring, slightly fragrant.
Longevity: 15-20 days. ∘ *Inflorescence:* 10-15cm; zigzag, erect or arcuate.

Distribution: southern China (Yunnan) to Vietnam

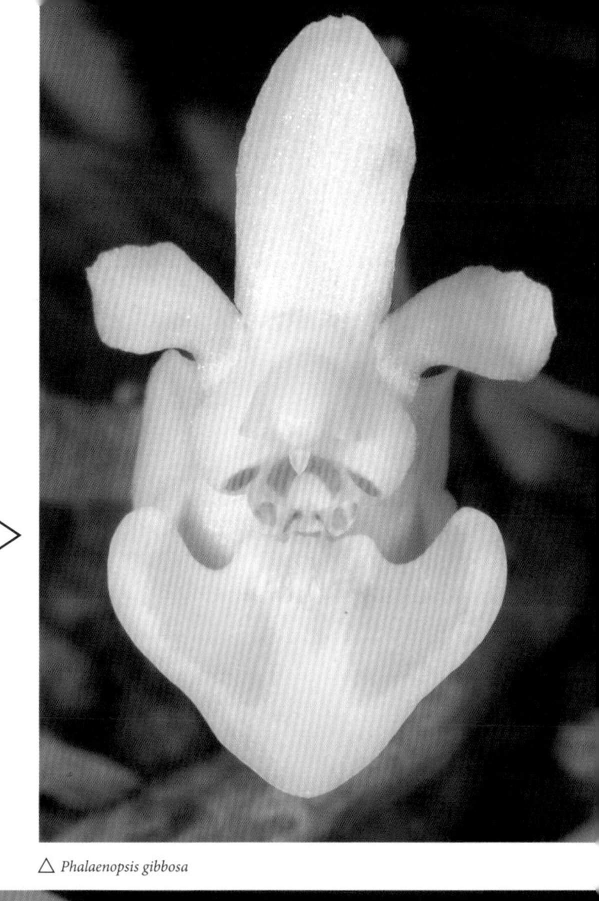

△ *Phalaenopsis gibbosa*

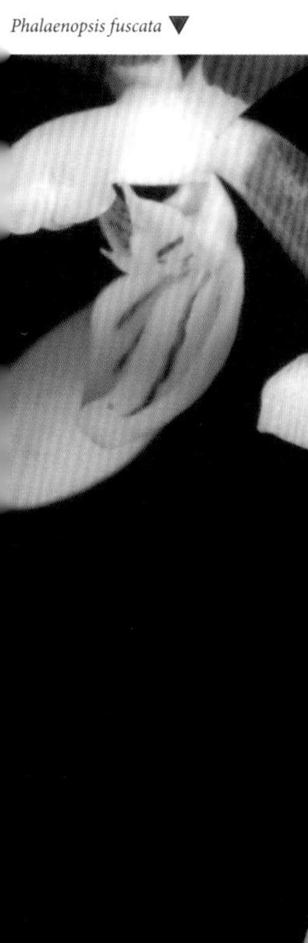

Phalaenopsis fuscata ▼

◀ *Phalaenopsis gigantea*

J.J. Smith, *Bulletin de Département de l'Agriculture aux Indes Néerlandaises, Buitenzorg,* **22**: 45 (1909).

Subgenus: *Phalaenopsis,* Section: *Polychilos*

P. gigantea has the largest plant size of the genus.

Habitat: Understory epiphyte in canopy of lowland to hill rain forests at elevations between 0-400 meters.

Culture: Difficult; warm-hot, moderate light.
Temperature: 23-32°C ◦ *Humidity:* 80-87%

Flowers: 3.7-7cm; Spring-Autumn, strongly fragrant.
Longevity: 20-25 days. ◦ *Inflorescence:* 15-40cm; racemose or paniculate, pendulous; can reflower for several seasons.

Distribution: eastern Indonesia (Borneo, Sabah & Sarawak)

Phalaenopsis hieroglyphica ▷

(Rchb.f.) H.R. Sweet, *American Orchid Society Bulletin,* **38**: 36 (1969).

Subgenus: *Phalaenopsis,* Section: *Polychilos*

Habitat: Growing on and hangs down from trees in cool and deeply shady locations of humid forests at elevations below 500 meters.

Culture: Easy; warm, low light.
Temperature: 23-30°C ◦ *Humidity:* 83-90%

Flowers: 5-8.75cm; Autumn, slightly fragrant.
Longevity: 25-30 days. ◦ *Inflorescence:* 30cm; suberect to arching, racemose or paniculate, branched; can reflower year after year.

Distribution: The Philippines (Polillo, Mindanao and Palawan)

△ *Phalaenopsis heiroglyphica* ▽

Phalaenopsis gigantea

Phalaenopsis honghenensis

F.Y. Liu, *Acta Botanica Yunnanica,* **13**: 373 (1991).

Subgenus: *Parishianæ,* Section: *Aphyllæ*

Habitat: Elevations of 2,000 meters, as a miniature sized, cool growing epiphyte with warty roots.

Culture: Easy; suitable for low temperature cultivation, bright light. *Temperature:* 0-25°C ◦ *Humidity:* 60-80%

Flowers: 2.5-3.0cm; Early Spring, strongly fragrant.
Longevity: 15-25 days. ◦ *Inflorescence:* 7-8cm; simple.

Distribution: southern China (Yunnan) and Thailand to Vietnam

Phalaenopsis inscriptiosinensis

Fowlie, *Orchid Digest,* **47**: 11 (1983).

Subgenus: *Parishianæ,* Section: *Aphyllæ*

This species is often cited as a synonym of *P. sumatrana,* but differs in having smaller flowers, no tuft of hairs on the distal tip of the labellum and the calli arise from a basal thickening.

Habitat: Epiphytic, on forests trees at elevations below 900 meters.

Culture: Slightly difficult; warm, moderate light.
Temperature: 18-28°C ◦ *Humidity:* 75-85%

Flowers: 2.5-3.5cm; Late Spring-Summer, strong unpleasant fragrance.
Longevity: 20-25 days. ◦ *Inflorescence:* 7-11 cm; simple, suberect.

Distribution: western Indonesia (Sumatra)

Phalaenopsis honghenensis

▲ *Phalaenopsis inscriptiosinensis* ▼

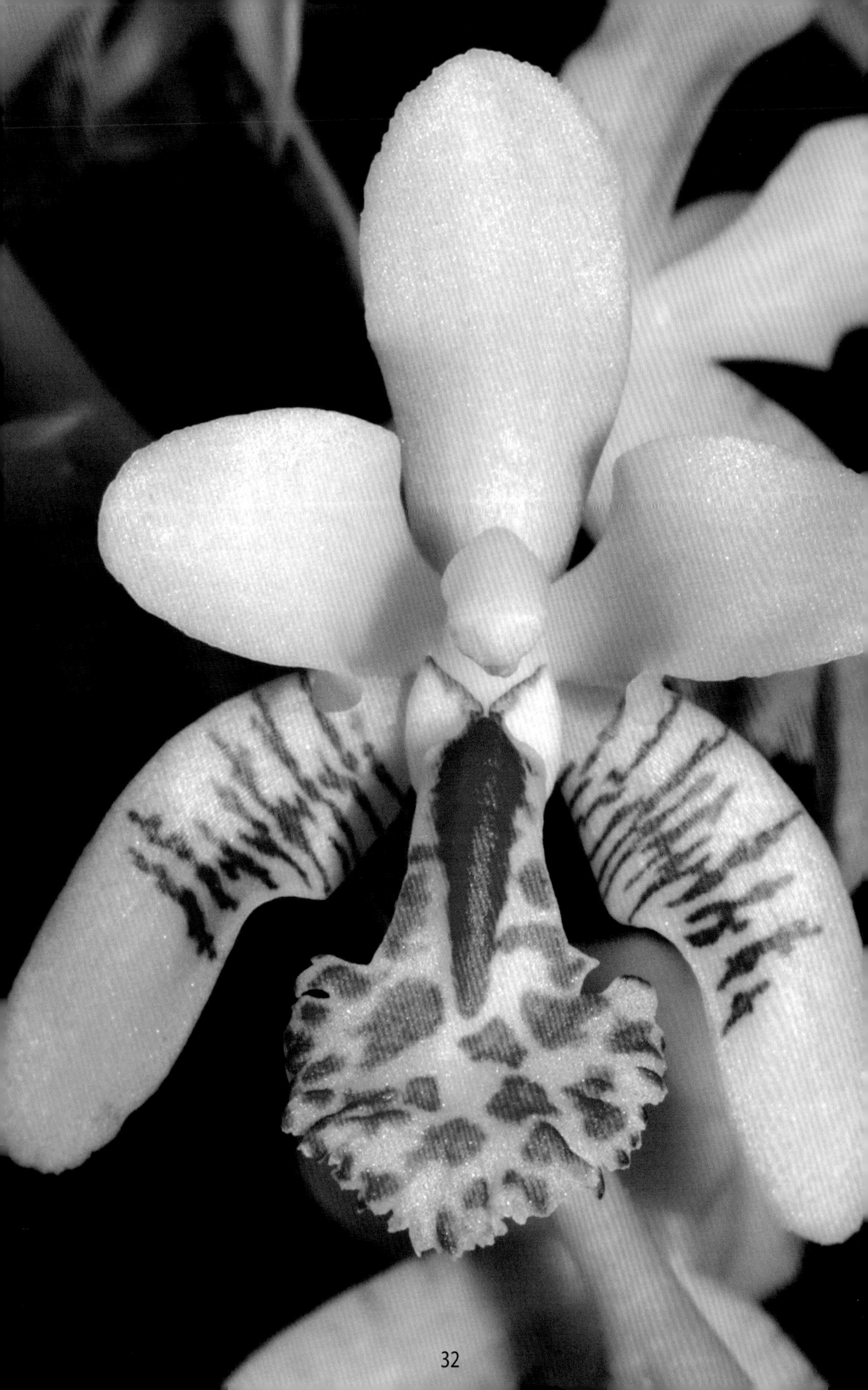

◁ *Phalaenopsis japonica*

(Reichenbach f.) Kocyan & Schuiteman, *Phytotaxa,* **161**(1): 67 (2014).

Subgenus: *Hygrochilus*

Habitat: On tree trunks in open sub-tropical forests or cliffs along valleys at elevations of 600-1,400 meters.

Culture: Easy; cool temperatures, high humidity with good air circulation and moderate light.
Temperature: 10-17°C ◦ ***Humidity:*** 50% or higher.

Flowers: 3cm; Early Spring, strongly fragrant.
Longevity: 25-30 days. ◦ ***Inflorescence:*** 18cm; branches arching, pendulous.

Distribution: southern China (Yunnan & Zhejiang) and Korea (Jeollanam-do) to southern Japan (Ryukyu Islands)

Phalaenopsis javanica ▶

J.J. Smith, *Bulletin de Département de l'Agriculture aux Indes Néerlandaises, Buitenzorg,* ser. 2, **26**: 77 (1918).

Subgenus: *Phalaenopsis,* Section: *Polychilos*

Habitat: Endemic to western Java at elevations from 700-1,000 meters (extinct in nature).

Culture: Easy; hot-warm, medium light.
Temperature: 23-32°C ◦ ***Humidity:*** 70-80%

Flowers: 3-5cm; Spring-early Fall, slightly fragrant.
Longevity: 15-20 days. ◦ ***Inflorescence:*** 25cm; suberect, racemose and sometimes branching.

Distribution: western Indonesia (Java)

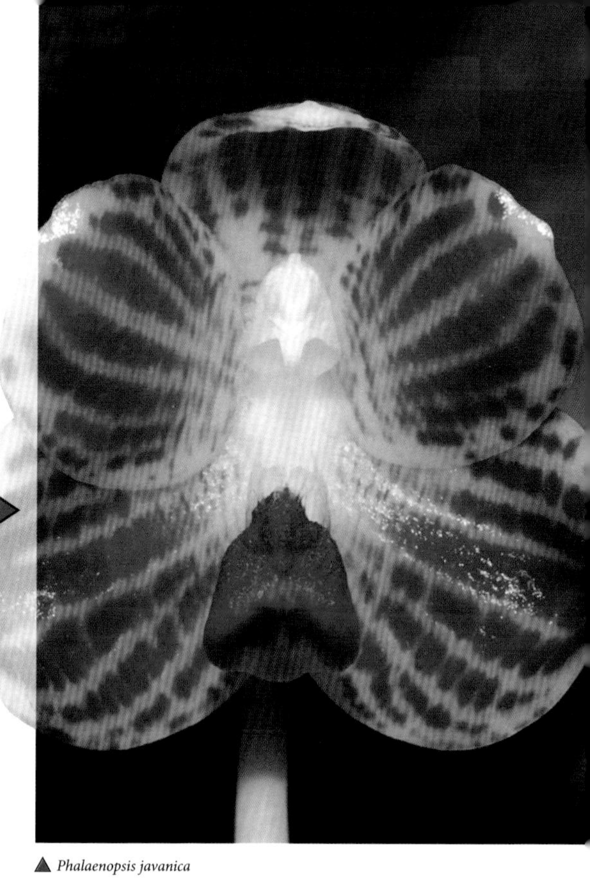

▲ *Phalaenopsis javanica*

Phalaenopsis japonica ▽

Phalaenopsis kunstleri

Hooker f., *Flora of British India,* **6**: 30 (1890).

Subgenus: *Phalaenopsis,* Section: *Polychilos*

Very similar with *P. fuscata,* but differs primarily by its squat column that is constricted at the middle and some details in the posterior callus.

Habitat: Low to moderate elevations in humid, lowland forests at 300-1,800 meters.

Culture: Easy; hot-cool, requires a little less light than other species. *Temperature:* 22-32°C ◦ *Humidity:* 75-82%

Flowers: 3.5-4cm; Early Spring-Summer, faintly fragrant at night to not fragrant. *Longevity:* 15-20 days. ◦ *Inflorescence:* 40cm; suberect to arching, paniculate simple or seldom branched.

Distribution: Myanmar to Malaysia

Phalaenopsis lindenii

Loher, *Le Journal des Orchidées,* **6**: 103 (1895).

Subgenus: *Phalaenopsis,* Section: *Phalaenopsis*

This species differs from *P. equestris* by the marbling of the foliage, the green stalk, and the orbicular and apiculate midlobe.

Habitat: Small sized; pendant, epiphyte growing up to 1,000-1,500 meters, precise locality not provided.

Culture: Easy; cool, moderate light. *Temperature:* 15-25°C ◦ *Humidity:* 80-90%

Flowers: 3-4cm; Peaks end of Spring, slightly fragrant. *Longevity:* 15-25 days. ◦ *Inflorescence:* 50cm; racemose or rarely paniculate, simple.

Distribution: the Philippines

▲ *Phalaenopsis lindenii*

◀ *Phalaenopsis kunstleri* ▼

◁ *Phalaenopsis lobbii*

(Rchb.f.) H.R. Sweet, *Genera Phalaenopsis,* 53 (1980).

Subgenus: *Phalaenopsis,* Section: *Polychilos*

Often confused with *P. parishii*, however, it differs by the structure of the lip.

Habitat: Piedmont or evergreen lowland forests, on rough barked trees or humid, mossy, mixed and coniferous forests on mossy branches of old gnarled trees at 360-1,200 meters.

Culture: Easy; warm-hot, requires more light than most other species. *Temperature:* 10-30°C ◦ *Humidity:* 60-85%

Flowers: 2-2.5cm; Winter-Spring, strongly fragrant. *Longevity:* 15-20 days. ◦ *Inflorescence:* 10cm; racemose or paniculate.

Distribution: southern China (Yunnan), northern India and Myanmar to Vietnam

Phalaenopsis lowii ▷

Reichenbach f., *Botanische Zeitung (Berlin),* **20**: 214 (1862).

Subgenus: *Parishianæ,* Section: *Aphyllæ*

This species has deciduous leaves when exposed to cold.

Habitat: Tropical deciduous seasonal forest on low limestone hills whose elevation does not exceed 60 meters.

Culture: Easy; cool-warm, requires more light than the majority of species and high humidity must be maintained. *Temperature:* 18-35°C ◦ *Humidity:* 61-90%

Flowers: 3-5 cm; Early Fall, faintly fragrant. *Longevity:* 15-25 days. ◦ *Inflorescence:* 25-38cm; branched, racemose or rarely paniculate.

Distribution: southern Myanmar to Thailand

▽ *Phalaenopsis lobbii* △

Phalaenopsis lowii ▷

◀ *Phalaenopsis luddemanniana*

Reichenbach f., *Botanische Zeitung (Berlin)*, **23**: 146 (1865).

Subgenus: *Phalaenopsis*, Section: *Polychilos*

Habitat: Humid, lowland tropical forests, in elevations usually below 100 meters.

Culture: Easy; hot, moderate light.
Temperature: 18-3°C ◦ *Humidity:* 80-90%

Flowers: 5-6cm; really large, Spring-Summer, strongly to sometimes fragrant. *Longevity:* 25-30 days. ◦
Inflorescence: 40cm; suberect, arcuate to pendent, racemose or paniculate, green, viable inflorescence will rebloom, has a habit of making keikis.

Distribution: the Philippines

Phalaenopsis maculata ▷

Reichenbach f., *Gardeners' Chronicle, n.s.*, **16**: 134 (1881).

Subgenus: *Phalaenopsis*, Section: *Polychilos*

Habitat: Epiphyte or lithophyte in wetlands to mixed forests at elevations of 200-1,000 meters on limestone hills at the base of mossy trees on moist, bare rocks.

Culture: Difficult; warm-cool, requires more light than other species, addition of calcium carbonate favors this species. *Temperature:* 18-30°C ◦ *Humidity:* 80-88%

Flowers: 3-3.5cm; Summer; not fragrant.
Longevity: 20-30 days. ◦ *Inflorescence:* 5-10cm; arched, racemose.

Distribution: Malaysia to eastern Indonesia (Borneo)

Phalaenopsis luddemanniana

△ *Phalaenopsis maculata* ▽

◁ *Phalaenopsis malipoensis*

Z.J. Liu & S.C. Chen, *Acta Botanica Yunnanic,* **27**: 37 (2005).

Subgenus: *Parishianæ,* Section: *Parishianæ*

Similar to *P. gibossa* it differs by a straight rachis, and much larger callus at the base of a deeply forked midlobe.

Habitat: Epiphytic on trees in sparse forests and on forest margins at elevations of 600-1,300 meters.

Culture: Easy; cool-intermediate, moderate light.
Temperature: 5-27°C ◦ *Humidity:* 54-82%

Flowers: 1.5-2cm; Spring, not fragrant.
Longevity: 15-20 days. ◦ *Inflorescence:* 8-15cm; racemose.

Distribution: southern China (Yunnan) and northern India (Assam)

Phalaenopsis mannii ▷

Reichenbach f., *Gardeners' Chronicle,* **1871**: 902 (1871).

Subgenus: *Phalaenopsis,* Section: *Polychilos*

Habitat: Epiphytic on rough wood of very wet evergreen, broadleaf forests with dense undergrowth near streams and river banks, found at 500-1,500 meters.

Culture: Easy; intermediate-warm, slightly less light.
Temperature: 10-30°C ◦ *Humidity:* 58-85%

Flowers: 3-5cm; Late Spring-early Summer, slightly fragrant.
Longevity: 15-25 days. ◦ *Inflorescence:* 45cm; pendulous, racemose or rarely paniculate.

Distribution: northeastern India, Nepal, southern China (Yunnan), Myanmar and Vietnam

△ *Phalaenopsis malipoensis* ▽

Phalaenopsis mannii ▷

Phalaenopsis mariae

Burbridge ex R.Warner & H.Williams,
Orchid Album, **2**: t. 80 (1883).

Subgenus: *Phalaenopsis,* Section: *Polychilos*

Can be confused with *P. bastianii.* The unique characteristics of *P. mariae* are; a pendent inflorescence; a precipitous raised keel on the midlobe, and the leaves/flower stems are freshly green to dark green, This species seldom has keikis.

Habitat: Epiphyte in dense shade at elevations up to 600 meter

Culture: Difficult; warm-hot, moderate light.
Temperature: 18-28°C • ***Humidity:*** 85-88%

Flowers: 4-4.5cm; Late Spring-early summer, strongly fragrant. ***Longevity:*** 25-30 days. • ***Inflorescence:*** 5cm; simple or multiple branched, pendent.

Distribution: eastern Indonesia (Borneo) to the Philippines

Phalaenopsis marriottiana

(Reichenbach f.) Kocyan & Schuiteman,
Phytotaxa, **161**(1): 67 (2014).

Subgenus: *Hygrochilus*

Habitat: Found on limestone cliffs and in deciduous montane forests and foothills, at elevations of 1,300 meters.

Culture: Easy; warm, bright-very strong light.
Temperature: 16-26°C • ***Humidity:*** 62-85%

Flowers: 3.5-5cm; Winter-Spring, strange floral fragrance.
Longevity: 1-2 months. • ***Inflorescence:*** 45cm; suberect, arcuate.

Distribution: southern China (Yunnan), northern India (Assam), Myanmar to Vietnam

▲ *Phalaenopsis mariae*

▽ *Phalaenopsis marriottiana*

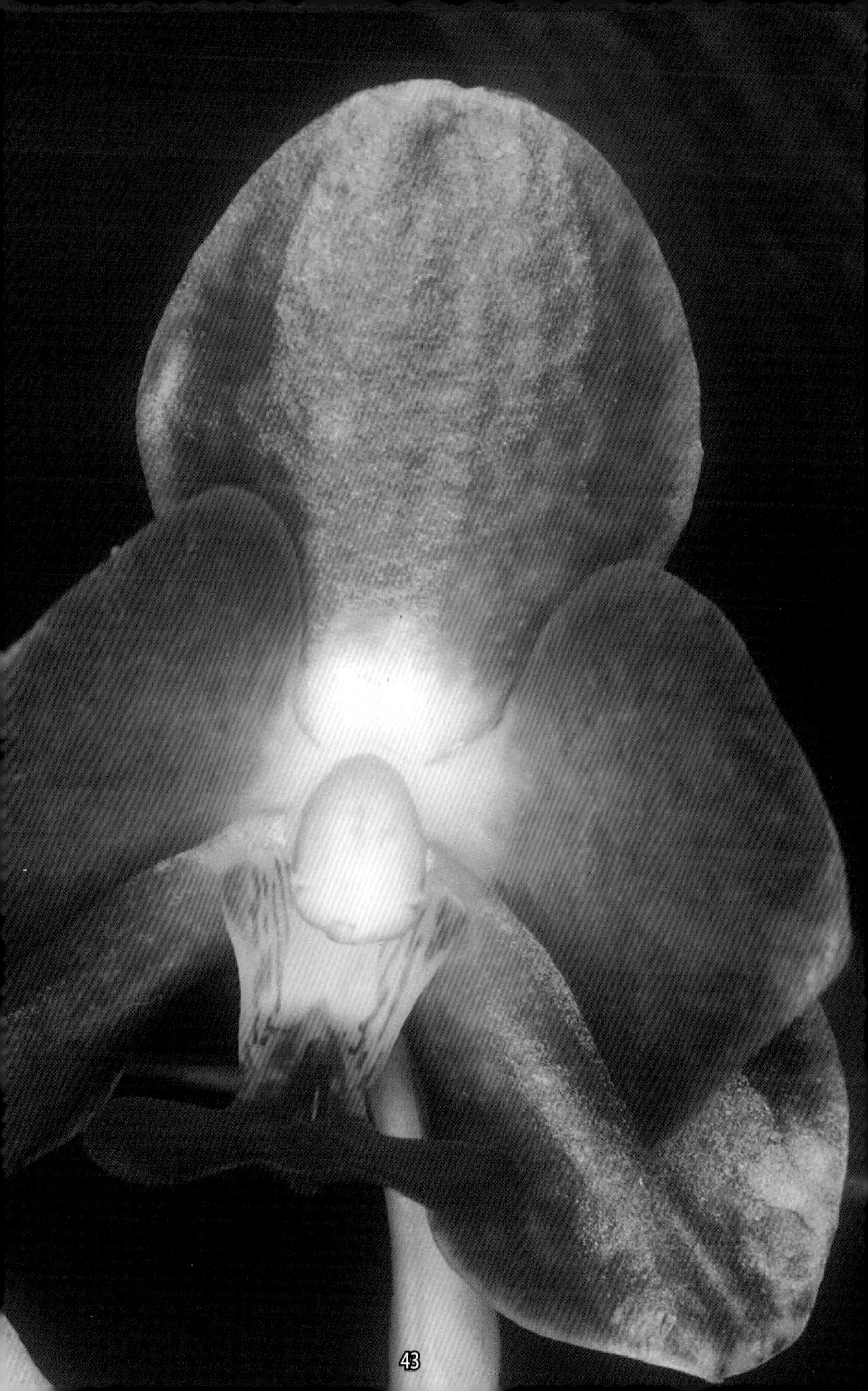

◁ *Phalaenopsis mentawaiensis*

O. Gruss, *Die Orchidee*, **65**(3): 238 (2014).

Subgenus: *Phalaenopsis,* Section: *Polychilos*

When compared to *P. violacea*, *P. mentawaiensis* has a long, rounded rachis up to 50cm long that can reach over the narrower leaves. The species has finer roots, as well as significantly larger, brilliantly colored flowers.

Habitat: On tall trees around riverine forests, at elevations of 0-100 meters.

Culture: Easy; warm-hot, bright light.
Temperature: 22-32°C ◦ ***Humidity:*** 80-86%

Flowers: 4.5-5.2cm; Summer-early Fall, slightly fragrant, but is similar to *P. violacea*. ***Longevity:*** 30-40 days. ◦ *Inflorescence:* 15-50cm; inclined to erect, sometimes branched.

Distribution: Indonesia (Sumatra - Mentawai Archipelago)

▽ *Phalaenopsis micholitzii*

Rolfe, *Gardeners' Chronicle*, ser. 3, **8**: 197 (1890).

Subgenus: *Phalaenopsis,* Section: *Polychilos*

Habitat: Found low on tree trunks or near rivers at elevations of 50-900 meters.

Culture: Little difficult; warm-hot, moderate light.
Temperature: 19-32°C ◦ ***Humidity:*** 75-85%

Flowers: 3.5-6cm; Autumn-Spring, slightly fragrant.
Longevity: 25-35 days. ◦ ***Inflorescence:*** 1-5cm; suberect.

Distribution: the Philippines

▲ *Phalaenopsis mentawaiensis*

▽ *Phalaenopsis micholitzii* ▷

◁ *Phalaenopsis mirabilis*

(Seidenfaden) Schuiteman, *Orchideen Journal,* **14**: 62 (2007).

Subgenus: *Parisihianæ*, Section: *Deliciosæ*

Habitat: Epiphyte beside rivers in primary montane forest, at elevations between 680-1,300 meters.

Culture: Easy; hot-warm, low-moderate light.
Temperature: 10-24°C ● *Humidity:* 45-83%

Flowers: 0.7cm; Fall, unknown fragrance.
Longevity: 1 day. ● *Inflorescence:* 8-10cm; pendent.

Distribution: southern China (Yunnan) to Thailand

Phalaenopsis modesta ▶

J.J. Smith, *Icones Bogorienses (Leiden),* t. 218 (1906).

Subgenus: *Phalaenopsis,* Section: *Polychilos*

Habitat: Hills and low montane forests usually low down or on the base and roots of trees near streams at elevations around 50-900 meters.

Culture: Easy; hot-humid, low-moderate light.
Temperature: 20-30°C ● *Humidity:* 80-90%

Flowers: 2-3.5cm; Spring-Fall, strongly fragrant.
Longevity: 20-25 days. ● *Inflorescence:* 12.5-15cm; racemose, arching to pendent often branching.

Distribution: eastern Indonesia (Borneo and Sabah)

△ *Phalaenopsis mirabilis*

▼ *Phalaenopsis modesta* ▶

◁ *Phalaenopsis mysorensis*

C.J. Saldanha, *Indian Forester,* **100**: 571 (1974).

Subgenus: *Parishianæ,* Section: *Deliciosæ*

As a water conservation measure, *P. mysorensis* shed their leaves during the drought period.

Habitat: Small branches covered by wet and moist mosses in windswept, stunted summit forests of isolated hills to elevations of 1,800 meters.

Culture: Difficult; warm-hot, moderate light.
Temperature: 14-34°C ◦ *Humidity:* 58-82%

Flowers: 1-1.5cm; Fall-early Spring, not fragrant. *Longevity:* not reported. ◦ *Inflorescence:* 1-8cm; between the leaves, terete.

Distribution: southern India (Karnataka) and Sri Lanka

Phalaenopsis natmataugensis

(T. Yukawa, Nob. Tanaka & J. Murata) Dalström & Ormerod, *Orchids (West Palm Beach),* **79**: 706 (2010).

Subgenus: *Parishianæ,* Section: *Aphyllæ*

P. natmataungensis, closely related to *P. stobartiana,* but can be distinguished from the latter by its mottled sepals and petals, the differently-shaped ridge of the lateral lobes of labellum. Leaves usually absent at flowering.

Habitat: Seasonable subtropical primarily forest at 1,740 meters.

Culture: Easy; cool-intermediate, moderate light.
Temperature: 9-27°C ◦ *Humidity:* 50-88%

Flowers: 3cm; Spring, fragrant. *Longevity:* Unreported. ◦ *Inflorescence:* 3.5-10.5cm; suberect pendent.

Distribution: northern Myanmar (Chin)

△ *Phalaenopsis mysorensis*

▽ *Phalaenopsis natmataugensis* ▷

◁ Phalaenopsis pallens

(Lindley) Reichenbach f., *Annales Botanices Systematicae,* **6**: 932 (1864).

Subgenus: *Phalaenopsis,* Section: *Polychilos*

Similar to *P. lueddemanniana,* but is distinguished by the callus which has two forward facing bifid projections, with one in front of the other.

Habitat: Lowland forests of the Philippines at around 500 meters.

Culture: Easy; intermediate-warm, low-moderate light. *Temperature:* 23-32°C ◦ *Humidity:* 80-88%

Flowers: 3.5-5cm; Summer-Autumn (irregular), not fragrant. *Longevity:* 25-35 days. ◦ *Inflorescence:* 12-17cm; racemose or paniculate; can rebloom for several years.

Distribution: the Philippines (Luzon, Bataan & Lanao)

Phalaenopsis pantherina ▷

(Lindley) Reichenbach f., *Botanische Zeitung (Berlin),* **22**: 298 (1864).

Subgenus: *Phalaenopsis,* Section: *Polychilos*

Habitat: Tall, high canopy trees, in lowland to mixed montane rain forests, 0-800 meters, exposed to bright light.

Culture: Easy; warm-hot, moderate-strong light. *Temperature:* 24-32°C ◦ *Humidity:* 79-84%

Flowers: 5-6cm; Spring-Autumn (irregular), faintly to somewhat sweetly fragrant. *Longevity:* 25-30 days. ◦ *Inflorescence:* 20-45cm; erect, racemose or branched.

Distribution: eastern Indonesia (Borneo) and Labuan Islands

△ *Phalaenopsis pallens*

▼ *Phalaenopsis pantherina* ▶

◀ *Phalaenopsis parishii*

Reichenbach f., *Botanische Zeitung (Berlin)*, **23**: 146 (1865).

Subgenus: *Parishianæ,* Section: *Parishianæ*

Habitat: Very damp locations, growing on the branches of trees hanging over the river at lower elevations to 500 meters.

Culture: Easy; hot, moderate light.
Temperature: 20-35°C ◦ *Humidity:* 60-90%

Flowers: 1.5-2.0cm; Spring, strongly fragrant.
Longevity: 15-20 days. ◦ *Inflorescence:* 5-14cm; arching, racemose or rarely paniculate.

Distribution: northeastern India (Assam), Nepal and Myanmar to Vietnam

Phalaenopsis philippinensis ▷

Golamco ex Fowlie & C.Z. Tang, *Orchid Digest*, **51**: 92 (1987).

Subgenus: *Phalaenopsis,* Section: *Phalaenopsis*

Habitat: Forms colonies on the main branches of trees around the river banks of the Sierra Madre, 0-1,200 meters.

Culture: Easy; warm, moderate light.
Temperature: 13-25°C ◦ *Humidity:* 85-94%

Flowers: 7.0-9.0cm; Spring, slightly fragrant.
Longevity: 25-30 days. ◦ *Inflorescence:* 1.20cm; erect to semi-pendulous, freely branching.

Distribution: the Philippines (Luzon)

▲ *Phalaenopsis parishii* ▼

Phalaenopsis philippinensis ▷

◁ *Phalaenopsis pulcherrima*

(Lindley) J.J. Smith, *Repertorium Specierum Novarum Regni Vegetabilis,* **32**: 366 (1933).

Subgenus: *Parishianæ,* Section: *Esmeralda*

P. pulcherrima requires more light than other species and flowers more in the summer.

Habitat: Clump forming lithophyte or terrestrial found in sandy soils at elevations of 100-1,300 meters in evergreen, lowland forests along canyons of montane streams and river banks in bright humid environments.

Culture: Easy; hot-warm, strong light.
Temperature: 7-32°C ◦ *Humidity:* 55-60%

Flowers: 2-3cm; Summer-Fall, not fragrant.
Longevity: 15-19 days. ◦ *Inflorescence:* 50-90cm; erect.

Distribution: northeastern India (Assam), eastern China (Hainan), Myanmar to Vietnam

Phalaenopsis pulchra ▶

(Reichenbach f.) H.R. Sweet, *American Orchid Society Bulluten,* **37**: 1102 (1968).

Subgenus: *Phalaenopsis,* Section: *Polychilos*

Habitat: Epiphytic species found on eastern mountain slopes at elevations of 100-650 meters.

Culture: Easy; warm, moderate light.
Temperature: 12-25°C ◦ *Humidity:* 85-90%

Flowers: 4.0-6.0cm; Spring-Summer, not fragrant.
Longevity: 25-30 days. ◦ *Inflorescence:* 10-25cm; suberect to arcuate, racemose or paniculate; may produce apical keikis instead of flowers.

Distribution: the Philippines

△ *Phalaenopsis pulcherrima* ▽

Phalaenopsis pulchra ▶

◁ *Phalaenopsis regnieriana*

Reichenbach f., *Gardeners' Chronicle,* **1887**(2): 746 (1887).

Subgenus: *Parishianæ,* Section: *Esmeralda*

Flowers are similar to those of *P. pulcherrima,* but differs by having a bifide callus and a very small lobules.

Habitat: Terrestrial or lithophytic, a clump forming species found in subtropical rain forests, at elevations of 0-150 meters.

Culture: Easy; intermediate-warm, moderate-strong light.
Temperature: 14-35°C ◦ ***Humidity:*** 50-60%

Flowers: 2-2.5cm; Summer-Fall, not fragrant.
Longevity: 10-15 days. ◦ ***Inflorescence:*** 50-60cm; erect.

Distribution: Thailand

Phalaenopsis reichenbachiana ▶

Reichenbach f. & Sander, *Gardeners' Chronicle,* n.s., **18**: 586 (1882).

Subgenus: *Phalaenopsis,* Section: *Polychilos*

Habitat: Epiphytes found around river banks from 0-500 meters.

Culture: Easy; hot-warm, moderate light.
Temperature: 24-32°C ◦ ***Humidity:*** 70-80%

Flowers: 4-5cm; Late Spring-Summer, faintly fragrant.
Longevity: 25-35 days. ◦ ***Inflorescence:*** Up to 45cm; erect or arcuate, sometimes branches.

Distribution: the Philippines (Mindanao)

Phalaenopsis regnieriana

▼ *Phalaenopsis reichenbachiana* ▲

△ Phalaenopsis robinsonii

J.J. Smith, *Philippine Journal Science, C,* **12**: 259 (1917).

Subgenus: *Phalaenopsis,* Section: *Polychilos*

Habitat: Epiphytic on tree trunks away from direct sunlight at 600 meters, in shady, humid forests with year round rainfall.

Culture: Easy; warm, moderate light.
Temperature: 23-33°C ◦ ***Humidity:*** 70-85%

Flowers: 3-4cm; Fall, not fragrant.
Longevity: Unreported. ◦ ***Inflorescence:*** 19-20cm; suberect or arcuate, branched, shorter than the foliage.

Distribution: eastern Indonesia (Maluku -Ambon)

Phalaenopsis rundumensis ▶

P.J. Cribb & A.L. Lamb, *Malesian Orchid Journal*, **9**: 51 (2012).

Subgenus: *Phalaenopsis,* Section: *Polychilos*

Very similar to *P. doweryensis* and *P. gigantea*, but has an unusual flowering habit in which the flowers appear in groups of threes rather than simultaneously.

Habitat: Epiphyte in canopy of rain forests at elevations of 600-800 meters.

Culture: Difficult in culture; warm-hot, moderate light. ***Temperature:*** 23-32°C ◦ ***Humidity:*** 80-87%

Flowers: 4.5cm; Fall, not fragrant.
Longevity: 20-25 days. ◦ ***Inflorescence:*** Up to 20cm; pendent, a little shorter than the longest leaf.

Distribution: eastern Indonesia (Borneo - Sabah)

△ *Phalaenopsis robinsonii* ▼ *Phalaenopsis rundumensis* ▶

Phalaenopsis sanderiana

Reichenbach f., *Flora*, **65**: 466 (1882).

Subgenus: *Phalaenopsis*, Section: *Phalaenopsis*

Habitat: On branches of trees covered with moss and subjected to great heat and moisture, found between 0-500 meters.

Culture: Easy; warm-hot, moderate light.
Temperature: 20-32°C ∘ ***Humidity:*** 80-85%

Flowers: 5-8.5cm; Spring-Summer, not fragrant.
Longevity: 25-30 days. ∘ ***Inflorescence:*** 80cm; arching-erect, racemose or few branched paniculate.

Distribution: the Philippines (Mindanao)

Phalaenopsis schilleriana

Reichenbach f., *Hamburger Garten-Blumenzeitung*, **16**: 115 (1860).

Subgenus: *Phalaenopsis*, Section: *Phalaenopsis*

Habitat: High up on trees along wet, woody slopes, at elevations of 0-400 meters.

Culture: Easy; warm-hot, moderate light.
Temperature: 18-32°C ∘ ***Humidity:*** 80-90%

Flowers: 5.5-9cm; Late Winter-early Spring, faintly fragrant. ***Longevity:*** 20-30 days. ∘ ***Inflorescence:*** 90cm; ascending or sub-ascending.

Distribution: the Philippines

△ *Phalaenopsis sanderiana* ▽

Phalaenopsis schilleriana ▶

Phalaenopsis speciosa

Reichenbach f., *Gardeners' Chronicle, London,* n.s., **15**: 562 (1881).

Subgenus: *Phalaenopsis,* Section: *Polychilos*

Habitat: Epiphytes on mangroves in muddy swamps at low elevations of 0-500 meters. Now extinct in the wild.

Culture: Easy; hot-warm, moderate light.
Temperature: 25-33°C ◦ *Humidity:* 80% or more on Nicobar Island.

Flowers: 5-6 cm; Late Spring-early Winter; strongly fragrant.
Longevity: 25-30 days. ◦ *Inflorescence:* 20-30cm; arcuate or pendent, racemose or paniculate.

Distribution: eastern India (Andaman & Nicobar Islands)

Phalaenopsis stobartiana

Reichenbach f., *Gardeners' Chronicle, London,* n.s., **8**: 392 (1877).

Subgenus: *Parishianæ,* Section: *Aphyllæ*

The leaves are usually absent at flowering time.

Habitat: On large tree branches in very wet areas over streams in warm dense forest, in an extremely reduced ecological niche from 0-100 meters in some localities and 800-900 meters in others.

Culture: Easy; intermediate-warm, moderate light.
Temperature: 3-25°C ◦ *Humidity:* 60-80%

Flowers: 3.5-4cm; Spring, strongly fragrant.
Longevity: 15-25 days. ◦ *Inflorescence:* 20cm; racemose.

Distribution: southeastern China (Yunnan to Hainan)

◀ *Phalaenopsis speciosa*

▼ *Phalaenopsis stobartiana* ▲

◀ Phalaenopsis stuartiana

Reichenbach f., *Gardeners' Chronicle, London, n.s.*, **15**: 748 (1881).

SUBGENUS: *Phalaenopsis*, SECTION: *Phalaenopsis*

Habitat: Warm, humid forests around the rivers of the islands at elevations 0-500 meters.

Culture: Easy; hot-warm, moderate light.
Temperature: 22-30°C ◦ *Humidity:* 82-90%

Flowers: 5-7cm; Early Spring-Winter, strongly fragrant.
Longevity: 25-30 days. ◦ *Inflorescence:* 60cm; arcuate to pendent.

Distribution: the Philippines (Mindanao)

Phalaenopsis subparishii ▷

(Z.H. Tsi) Kocyan & Schuiteman, *Phytotaxa*, **161**(1): 67 (2014).

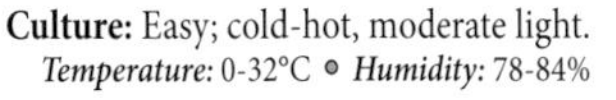

SUBGENUS: *Hygrochilus*

Habitat: On the trees of rock escarpments in pine forests at elevations of 300-1,100 meters.

Culture: Easy; cold-hot, moderate light.
Temperature: 0-32°C ◦ *Humidity:* 78-84%

Flowers: 4cm; Spring-early Summer, fragrant.
Longevity: 25-30 days. ◦ *Inflorescence:* 9-10cm; racemose.

Distribution: southern China (Zhejiang)

◀ *Phalaenopsis stuartiana* ▼

Phalaenopsis subparishii ▷

Phalaenopsis sumatrana

Korthals & Reichenbach f.,
Hamburger Garten-Blumenzeitung, **16**: 115 (1860).

Subgenus: *Phalaenopsis*, Section: *Polychilos*

Habitat: Epiphyte in lowland to mixed tropical montane forests and shady nooks near streams at elevations around 600-700 meters.

Culture: Easy; warm-hot, low-moderate light.
Temperature: 23-32°C • *Humidity:* 80-85%

Flowers: 4.5-7.5cm; Spring-Fall, slightly fragrant.
Longevity: 25-30 days. • *Inflorescence:* 30cm; arcuate or erect, racemose or branched.

Distribution: Myanmar to Vietnam, Malaysia, Indonesia (Sumatra to Boreno) and the Philippines (Palawan)

Phalaenopsis taenialis

(Lindley) Christenson & Pradhan,
Indian Orchid Journal, **1**: 154 (1985).

Subgenus: *Parishianæ*, Section: *Aphyllæ*

Habitat: Epiphytes on tree trunks in montane forests between 1,000-2,500 meters.

Culture: Difficult; cool-intermediate, low-moderate light.
Temperature: 3-28°C • *Humidity:* 60-80%

Flowers: 2-3 cm; Spring-early Summer, strongly fragrant.
Longevity: 15-25 days. • *Inflorescence:* 10cm; peduncle like, racemose.

Distribution: southern China (Yunnan), northeastern India (Assam), Bhutan, Nepal and Myanmar to Vietnam

▲ *Phalaenopsis sumatrana* ▼

Phalaenopsis taenialis ▷

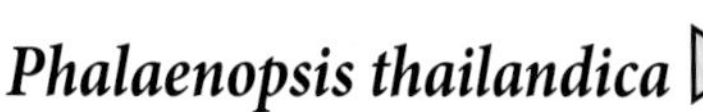

Phalaenopsis tetraspis

Reichenbach f., *Xenia Orchidaceæ*, **2**: 146 (1870).

Subgenus: *Phalaenopsis,* Section: *Polychilos*

Habitat: Found in very shady, dim forests and on mangroves above non-brackish water, at elevations of 0-400 meters.

Culture: Easy; hot-warm, moderate light.
Temperature: 25-30°C ◦ *Humidity:* 76-92%

Flowers: 4-6cm; Summer, strongly fragrant.
Longevity: 25-30 days. ◦ *Inflorescence:* 30-40cm; racemose or paniculate.

Distribution: eastern India (Andaman & Nicobar Islands) to western Indonesia (Sumatra)

Phalaenopsis thailandica

O. Gruss & Röeth, *Orchidee (Hamburg)*, **60**: 116 (2009).

Subgenus: *Parishianæ,* Section: *Parishianæ*

Habitat: Warm, humid lowland forests, 0 to 1,000 meters.

Culture: Easy; warm-hot, moderate light.
Temperature: 20-32°C ◦ *Humidity:* 60-80%

Flowers: 1.5cm; Late Winter-early Spring, slightly to not fragrant.
Longevity: 15-20 days. ◦ *Inflorescence:* 12cm; erect or arcuate, branched.

Distribution: Thailand

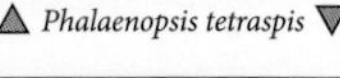

▲ *Phalaenopsis tetraspis* ▼

Phalaenopsis thailandica ▷

Phalaenopsis ubonensis

▲ Phalaenopsis venosa ▼

◀ *Phalaenopsis ubonensis*

O. Gruss, *Die Orchidee*, **65**(4): 318 (2014).

Subgenus: *Parishianæ,* Section: *Esmeralda*

Habitat: Terrestrial or lithophyte found in the lowland forests, at elevations of 150-400 meters.

Culture: Easy; warm, moderate-bright light.
Temperature: 18-36°C ◦ *Humidity:* 62-82%

Flowers: 5cm; Summer-Fall, not fragrant.
Longevity: 15-19 days. ◦ *Inflorescence:* 50-180cm; upright, partly branched.

Distribution: Thailand and Laos

Phalaenopsis venosa ▶

Shim & Fowlie, *Orchid Digest*, **47**: 125 (1983).

Subgenus: *Phalaenopsis,* Section: *Polychilos*

Habitat: Epiphytes in lowland forests at elevations from 450-1,000 meters.

Culture: Easy; warm-cool, low light.
Temperature: 18-28°C ◦ *Humidity:* 75-85%

Flowers: 4-6cm; Irregular flowering, mostly Spring-Autumn, strong unpleasant fragrance.
Longevity: 30-40 days. ◦ *Inflorescence:* 20-25 cm; erect.

Distribution: eastern Indonesia (Sulawesi)

Phalaenopsis violacea ▲

▼ Phalaenopsis viridis

▲ *Phalaenopsis violacea*

H. Witte, *Annales d'Horticulture et de Botanique ou Flore des Jardins du Royaume des Pays-Bas, Leiden,* **4**: 129 (1861).

SUBGENUS: *Phalaenopsis,* SECTION: *Polychilos*

Habitat: Pendulous epiphyte found in hot, wet, deep shade of large trees around the river lowlands at 0-150 meters.

Culture: Easy; warm, low-moderate light.
Temperature: 23-32°C ◦ ***Humidity:*** 81-86%

Flowers: 3.5-6cm; Spring-Autumn, has strongest fragrance of the *Phalaenopsis* species.
Longevity: 30-40 days. ◦ *Inflorescence:* 10-12.5cm; fractiflex.

Distribution: Malaysia to Indonesia (Sumatra)

◀ *Phalaenopsis viridis*

J.J. Smith, *Bulletin de Département de l'Agriculture aux Indes Néerlandaises, Buitenzorg,* **5**: 21 (1907).

SUBGENUS: *Phalaenopsis,* SECTION: *Polychilos*

Habitat: Lithophyte or epiphyte on rocks (limestone) or tree trunks in the shade of shrubs, elevation of 700-1,000 meters.

Culture: Easy; hot-warm, moderate light.
Temperature: 20-30°C ◦ ***Humidity:*** 75-85%

Flowers: 3-4cm; Spring, not fragrant.
Longevity: 20-25 days. ◦ *Inflorescence:* 60-70cm; erect, occasionally branching, reflowers for several years.

Distribution: eastern Indonesia (Sumatra)

Phalaenopsis wilsonii ▲ ▽ *Phalaenopsis yingjiangensis*

▲ *Phalaenopsis wilsonii*

Rolfe, *Bulletin Miscellaneous Information Kew,* **1909**: 65 (1909).

Subgenus: *Parishianæ,* Section: *Aphyllæ*

Habitat: Epiphytic/lithophytic found in shady, open forests zones constantly subjected to very strong moisture; at elevations varying from 800-2,150 meters.

Culture: Easy; warm-cool, moderate light (Plants are not deciduous in culture). ***Temperature:*** 0-25°C ◦ ***Humidity:*** 60-85%

Flowers: 2.5-5cm; Spring, fragrant.
Longevity: 15-25 days. ◦ ***Inflorescence:*** 20cm; arcuate or pendent.

Distribution: western China (Yunnan, Szechuan, eastern Tibet), Myanmar and Thailand

◁ *Phalaenopsis yingjiangensis*

(Z.H. Tsi) Kocyan & Schuiteman, *Phytotaxa,* **161**: (1): 67 (2014).

Subgenus: *Ornithochilus*

Habitat: On tree trunks in semi evergreen, broadleaf forests between 1,500-1,600 meters.

Culture: Easy; cool-intermediate, moderate light.
Temperature: 12-32°C ◦ *Humidity:* 45-95%

Flowers: 1-1.5cm; Summer, not fragrant.
Longevity: 20-25 days. ◦ *Inflorescence:* 20cm; branched, pendulous.

Distribution: southern China (Yunnan), northeastern India (Mizoram) and Thailand (Chiang Mai)

Phalaenopsis zheliangensis ▲

◀ *Phalaenopsis zheliangensis*

(Z.H. Tsi) Schuiteman, *Renziana,* **2**: 15 (2012).

Subgenus: *Parishianæ,* Section: *Aphyllæ*

This plant may lose its leaves in winter.

Habitat: Epiphytic on tree branches in sparse forests or found along forest margins at 300-900 meters.

Culture: Difficult; intermediate, moderate light.
Temperature: 8-30°C ◦ *Humidity:* 50-90%

Flowers: 1cm; Summer, not fragrant.
Longevity: 15-25 days. ◦ *Inflorescence:* 8-13cm; racemose.

Distribution: eastern China (Zhejiang, Guansu and Shaanxi)

Phalaenopsis Distribution

throughout southeast Asia

1. **P. amabilis** - Indonesia, the Philippines, New Guinea to northeastern Australia (Queensland)
2. **P. amboinensis** - eastern Indonesia (Sulawesi to Maluku)
3. **P. aphrodite** - southern Taiwan to the Philippines
4. **P. appendiculata** - Malaysia (Pahang)
5. **P. bastianii** - Philippines (Sulu Archipelago)
6. **P. bellina** - eastern Indonesia (Borneo)
7. **P. buyssoniana** - Thailand and Vietnam
8. **P. cacharensis** - northeastern India (Assam)
9. **P. celebensis** - eastern Indonesia (Sulawesi - Celebes)
10. **P. chibae** - Vietnam
11. **P. cochlearis** - Malaysia to eastern Indonesia (Borneo)
12. **P. corningiana** - eastern Indonesia (Borneo - Sarawak)
13. **P. cornu-cervi** - Myanmar to Vietnam, Malaysia, Indonesia to the Philippines
14. **P. deliciosa** - southern China (Yunnan) India, Sri Lanka, Nepal, Myanmar to Vietnam, Malaysia, Indonesia to the Philippines
15. **P. difformis** - southern China (Yunnan), northern India, Nepal, Myanmar to Vietnam, Malaysia to Indonesia
16. **P. doweryensis** - eastern Indonesia (Borneo - Sabah)
17. **P. equestris** - southern Taiwan (Hsiao & Lan Yü) to the Philippines
18. **P. fasciata** - the Philippines
19. **P. fimbriata** - western Indonesia
20. **P. finleyi** - Thailand and Vietnam
21. **P. floresensis** - eastern Indonesia (Lesser Sunda Islands)
22. **P. fuscata** - Malaysia, eastern Indonesia (Boreno), the Philippines
23. **P. gibbosa** - southern China (Yunnan), Laos to Vietnam
24. **P. gigantea** - eastern Indonesia (Borneo)
25. **P. hieroglyphica** - the Philippines
26. **P. honghenensis** - southern China (Yunnan), Thailand to Vietnam
27. **P. inscriptiosinensis** - western Indonesia (Sumatra)
28. **P. japonica** - southern China (Yunnan & Zhejiang), Korea (Jeollanam-do) to Japan
29. **P. javanica** - western Indonesia (Java)
30. **P. kunstleri** - Myanmar to Malaysia
31. **P. lindenii** - the Philippines
32. **P. lobbii** - southern China (Yunnan), northern India, Myanmar to Vietnam
33. **P. lowii** - Myanmar to Thailand
34. **P. lueddemanniana** - the Philippines
35. **P. luteola** - eastern Indonesia (Borneo)
36. **P. maculata** - Malaysia to eastern Indonesia (Borneo)
37. **P. malipoensis** - southern China (Yunnan)
38. **P. mannii** - northeastern India, Nepal, southern China (Yunnan), Myanmar and Vietnam
39. **P. mariae** - eastern Indonesia (Borneo) to the Philippines
40. **P. marriottiana** - northeastern India (Assam), southern China (Yunnan), Myanmar to Vietnam
41. **P. mentawaiensis** - Indonesia (Sumatra - Mentawai Archipelago)
42. **P. micholitzii** - the Philippines
43. **P. mirabilis** - Thailand
44. **P. modesta** - eastern Indonesia (Borneo)
45. **P. mysorensis** - southern India (Karnataka) and Sri Lanka
46. **P. natmataungensis** - northern Myanmar

4

47. **P. pallens** - the Philippines
48. **P. pantherina** - Borneo
49. **P. parishii** - northeastern India (Assam), Nepal, Myanmar to Vietnam
50. **P. philippinensis** - the Philippines (Luzon)
51. **P. pulcherrima** - northeastern India (Assam), eastern China (Hainan), Myanmar to Vietnam and Indonesia
52. **P. pulchra** - the Philippines
53. **P. regnieriana** - Thailand
54. **P. reichenbachiana** - the Philippines (Mindanao)
55. **P. robinsonii** - eastern Indonesia (Maluku - Ambon)
56. **P. rundumensis** - eastern Indonesia (Borneo - Sabah)
57. **P. sanderiana** - the Philippines
58. **P. schilleriana** - the Philippines
59. **P. speciosa** - eastern India (Andaman and Nicobar Islands)
60. **P. stobartiana** - eastern China (Hainan)
61. **P. stuartiana** - the Philippines
62. **P. subparishii** - southern China
63. **P. sumatrana** - Myanmar to Vietnam, Malaysia, Indonesia to the Philippines (Palawan)
64. **P. taenialis** - southern China (Yunnan), northeastern India (Assam), Bhutan, Nepal, Myanmar to Vietnam
65. **P. tetraspis** - eastern India (Andaman and Nicobar Islands) to western Indonesia (Sumatra)
66. **P. thailandica** - Thailand
67. **P. ubonensis** - Thailand and Laos
68. **P. venosa** - eastern Indonesia (Sulawesi)
69. **P. violacea** - Malaysia, Indonesia (Sumatra)
70. **P. viridis** - eastern Indonesia (Sumatra)
71. **P. wilsonii** - western China (Tibet), Myanmar and Thailand
72. **P. yingjiangensis** - southern China (Yunnan), northeastern India (Mizoram) and Thailand (Chiang Mai)
73. **P. zhejiangensis** - eastern China (Zhejiang)

Phalaenopsis Cultural Instructions

Phalaenopsis, the moth orchid, is perhaps the best orchid for growing in the home, and is also a favorite with greenhouse growers. Well-grown plants can flower often, sometimes with a few flowers throughout the year, though the main season is late winter into spring. Average home temperatures and conditions are usually sufficient. Flower stems on certain hybrids can be forced to rebloom by cutting the tip off after the initial flowering. Only healthy plants should be induced to flower repeatedly.

LIGHT is easy to provide for *phlaenopsis*. They grow easily in a bright window, with little or no sun. An east window is ideal in the home; shaded south or west windows are acceptable. In overcast, northern winter climates, a full south exposure may be needed. Artificial lighting can easily be provided. Four fluorescent tubes in one fixture supplemened by incandescent bulbs are placed 6 to 12 inches above the leaves, 12 to 16 hours a day, following natural day length. In a greenhouse, shade must be given; 70 to 85 percent shade, or between 1,000 and 1,500 foot-candles, is recommended. No shadow should be seen if you hold your hand one foot above a plant's leaves.

TEMPERATURES for *phalaenopsis* should usually be above 60°F at night, and range between 75° and 85°F or more during the day. Although higher temperatures force faster vegetative growth, higher humidity and air movement must accompany higher temperatures, the recommended maximum being 90° to 95°F, night temperatures to 55°F are desirable for several weeks in the autumn to initiate flower spikes. Fluctuating temperatures can cause bud drop on plants with buds ready to open.

WATER is especially critical for *phalaenopsis*. Because they have no major water-storage organs other than their leaves, they must never completely dry out. Plants should be thorougly watered and not watered again until nearly dry. In the heat of summer, in a dry climate, this may be every other day; in the winter, in a cool northern greenhouse, it may be every 10 days. Water only in the morning, so that the leaves dry by nightfall, to prevent rot.

HUMIDITY is important to *phalaenopsis*, the recommended humidity being between 50 and 80 percent. In humid climates, as in greenhouses, it is imperative that the humid air is moving. Leaves should be dry as soon as possible, always by nightfall. In the home, set the plants on trays of gravel partially filled with water, so that the pots never sit in water.

FERTILIZE on a regular schedule, especially if the weather is warm, when the plants are most often growing. Twice a month applications of high-nitrogen fertilizer (such as 30-l0-10) are appropriate where bark-based media are used. Otherwise, a balanced rertilizer is best. When flowering is desired, a high-phosphorus fertilizer (such as 10-30-20) can be applied to promote blooming. Some growers apply fertilizer at one-quarter strength with every watering; this is best for warm, humid conditions. When cooler, or under overcast conditions, fertilizer should be applied twice per month at weak strength.

POTTING is best done in the spring, immediately after flowering. *Phalaenopsis* plants must be potted in a porous mix. Potting is usually done every one to three years. Mature plants can grow in the same container until the potting medium starts to decompose, usually in two years. Root rot occurs if plants are left in a soggy medum. Seedlings usually grow fast enough to need repotting yearly, and should be repotted in a fine-grade medium. Mature plants are potted in a medium-grade mix. To repot, remove all the old medium from the roots, trim soft, rotted roots, and spread the remaining roots over a handful of medium

Line Drawing: *Phalaenopsis stuartiana*, Manual of Orchidaceous Plants, **7**: pg39a (1891).

in the bottom of a new pot. Fill the rest of the pot with medium, working it among the roots, so that the junction or the rools and the stem is at the top of the medium.

The American Orchid Society invites you to join us and learn about the world's most fascinating flowers and plants. Your membership entitles you to our monthly magazine *Orchids*, a free copy of theAOS Orchid Source Directory, a 50-percent discount coupon good toward the purchase of one of our cultural publications, a 10-percent discount on items purchased through our Web site's electronic store and reciprocal benefits at more than 200 botanical gardens and arboreta associated with the American Horticultural Society through its Reciprocal Admissions Program. All this and much more can be yours as a member of the AOS.

American Orchid Society
Fairchild Tropical Botanic Gardens
10901 Old Cutler Road
Coral Gables, Florida 33156
Phone: 305/740-2010 • E-mail: TheAOS@aos.org

P. amabilis, Lindenia, 2: t79 (1886) • *P. cornu-cervi*, Century of Orchidaceae, t178 (1867) • *P. rosea*, Orchids (Jennings), t27 (1875)

P. fuscata, Dictionnaire Iconographique Orchidées, t6 (1899) • *P. grandiflora*, Les Orcchidées, t34 (1860) • *P. japonica*, Botanical Magazine, 95: t5798 (1896)

P·H·A·L·A·E·N·O·P·S·I·S ETYMOLOGIES

Phalaenopsis - From the Greek for moth and looking like.

P. *amabilis* - From the Latin for lovely, enchanting.

P. *amboinensis* - Named for the Indonesian island of Ambon found in the lesser Sunda Archipelago.

P. *aphrodite* - For the Greek goddess of beauty and love.

P. *appendiculata* - From the Latin for appendages.

P. *bastianii* - Formed from first name of Bastian Röllke, son of Lutz Röllke.

P. *bellina* - From the Latin for cute, nice.

P. *buyssoniana* - For François du Buysson (1825-1906), a French count and author of *Orchidophile.*

P. *cacharensis* - Named for the Cachar district of northeastern India (Assam).

P. *celebensis* - Named for the Celebes Islands (Sulawesi) found in eastern Indonesia.

P. *chibae* - For Masaaki Chiba (1930-1994), a Japanese dermatologist and amateur botanist who discovered the type species.

P. *cochlearis* - From the Latin for spoon-shaped (lip).

P. *corningiana* - For Erastus Corning (1794-1874), an American businessman, politician and orchid enthusiast.

P. *cornu-cervi* - From the Latin for the antler-shaped flower.

P. *deliciosa* - From the Latin for delicate, sensitive.

P. *difformis* - From the Latin for different.

P. *doweryensis* - Named for the Dowery Orchid Nursery of Virgina (USA), where species was cultivated.

P. *equestris* - From the Latin for riding, one upon the other.

P. *fasciata* - From the Latin for striped, bandaged.

P. *fimbriata* - From the Latin for fringed.

P. *finleyi* - For Roy Wayne Finley (1952-), an American physican and orchid collector.

P. *floresensis* - Named for Flores Island found in the Lesser Sunda Archipelago of central Indonesia.

P. *fuscata* - From the Latin for brownish.

P. *gibbosa* - From the Latin for hunchback.

P. *gigantea* - From the Greek for gigantic.

P. *hieroglyphica* - From the Greek for color streaks or patterns.

P. *honghenensis* - Named for the Honghe region of southeastern Yunnan, China.

P. *inscriptiosinensis* - For the flower stripes that are reminiscent of Chinese chops.

P. *japonica* - For Japan where type species is found.

P. *javanica* - Named for Java an Indonesian Island.

P. *kunstleri* - For Hermann H. Kunstler (1837-1887), a German orchid and entomology collector and illustrator in Malaysia.

P. *lindenii* - For Jean Linden (1817-1898), a Belgian plant collector and nursery owner.

P. *lobbii* - For Thomas Lobb (1820-1894), an English orchid collector in India, Indonesia and the Philippines.

P. *lowii* - For Hugh Low (1824-1906), an English colonial administrator, naturalist, adventurer and orchid collector in the far east.

P. *lueddemanniana* - For Gustav Adolph Lüddemann (1821-1884), a German-born gardner for Jean-Pierre Pescatore in Paris.

P. *maculata* - From the Latin for spotted.

P. *malipoensis* - Named for the Malipo district, found in southeastern Yunnan, China.

P. *mannii* - For Gustav Mann (1836-1916), a German-born gardener at the Royal Botanic Gardens, Kew.

P. *mariae* - For Holy Mary Burbridge, the wife of Fredrick William Burbridge (1847-1905), an English orchid collector.

P. *marriottiana* - For William Henry Smith Marriott (1835-1924), an English baronet, orchid collector and lawyer from Down House, Blandford.

P. *mentawaiensis* - Named for the Mentawai archipelago, found in southwestern of Sumatra, Indonesia.

P. *micholitzii* - For Wilhelm Micholitz (1854-1932), a German orchid collector for Sander's Nursery.

P. *mirabilis* - From the Latin for miraculous, remarkable.

P. *modesta* - From the Latin for modest, insignificant.

P. *mysorensis* - Named for the town of Mysore, located in the southern Indian state of Karnataka.

P. natmataungensis - Named for the area Natma Taung, found in the Chin state of western Myanmar.

P. pallens - From the Latin for pale.

P. pantherina - Greek for spotted like a leopard.

P. parishii - For Charles Samuel Pollock Parish (1822-1897), an English missionary and avid orchid collector in India and Myanmar.

P. philippinensis - From the Latin for occurring in the Philippines.

P. pulcherrima - From the Latin for very beautiful.

P. pulchra - From the Latin for beautiful.

P. regnieriana - For Alexandre Régnier (1843-x), a French orchid collector and nursery owner loacted at Fontenay-sous-Bois, Seine.

P. reichenbachiana - For Heinrich Gustav Reichenbach (1823-1889), a German orchidologist.

P. robinsonii - For Charles Budd Robinson (1871-1913), an American botanist in the Philippines.

P. rundumensis - Named for the Rundum (Tenom District) region of Sabah (northern Borneo) where the type was collected.

P. sanderiana - For Henry Fredrick Conrad Sander (1847-1920), an English orchid gardener and nursery owner.

P. schilleriana - For Gustav Wilhelm (Consul) Schiller (1803-1870), a Germany orchid collector from Hamburg.

P. speciosa - From the Latin for handsome, outstanding.

P. stobartiana - For William Culley Stobart (1837-1899), an English coal, railway shareholder and orchid grower from Etherley Lodge, Darlington.

P. stuartiana - For Stuart Henry Low (1826-1890), an English naturalist and nurseryman at Clapton.

P. subparishii - From the Latin for almost like *parishii.*

P. sumatrana - Referring to the Indonesian island of Sumatra.

P. taenialis - From the Latin for bandage-like, shaped.

P. tetraspis - Greek for with four shield, plates.

P. thailandica - From the Latin for Thailand where type species is found.

P. ubonensis - Named for the Ubon province of southeastern Thailand.

P. venosa - From the Latin for with veins (in regard to the lip).

P. violacea - From the Latin for purple.

P. viridis - From the Latin for green.

P. wilsonii - For Ernest Henry Wilson (1876-1930), an English plant collector of Asian plant species.

P. yingjiangensis - Named for the Yingjiang region of southwestern Yunnan, China.

P. zhejiangensis - Named for the Zhejiang region of southeastern China.

A SPECIAL

Thank You

to all our photographers

Eric Hunt ❀ Ramon de los Santos ❀ Martin Guenther ❀ American Orchid Society ❀ Swiss Orchid Foundation ❀ Larry Johnson
Mauro Rosim ❀ Lucas Bytomski ❀ Brigitte Bertram ❀ Branka Forscek
Pixietoe ❀ Olaf Gruss ❀ Frankie Hondoyo ❀ Lloyd Gross ❀ Walter Riner
Hussain Ahmed Barbhuiya ❀ Tomohisa Yukawa ❀ Lourens Grobler
Llyod Gross ❀ Danny Ducreux ❀ Jun Aoyama ❀ Greg Allikas
Joao Lacerda ❀ Martino Pizzol ❀ Peter T. Lin ❀ Limin Kung, Jr.
Yanyong Punpreuk ❀ Eric Legac ❀ Kenth Esbensen ❀ Brian Monk

Page - Photographer

i - Aoyama
iii - Kung
iv - Kung
v - Monk
vi - Allikas
1 - Allikas
3 - Allikas
4 - Riner
5a - Santos
5b - Santos
6 - Guenther
7a - Ducreux
7b - Santos
8a - Guenther
8b - Santos
9 - Guenther
10 - Santos
11a - Guenther
11b - Bertram
12a - Barbhuiya
12b - Santos
13 - Santos
14 - Guenther
15a - Guenther
15b - Guenther
16 - Guenther
17a - Santos
17b - Guenther
18a - Guenther
18b - Guenther
19 - Grobler
20 - Guenther
21a - Santos
21b - Guenther
22a - Guenther
22b - Pixietoe
23 - Gross
24 - Yanyong
25a - Guenther
25b - Gross
26 - Guenther
27a - Hunt
27b - Hunt
28 - Guenther
29a - Santos
29b - Guenther
30 - Guenther
31a - Santos
31b - Guenther
32 - Hunt
33a - Guenther
33b - Hunt
34 - Guenther
35a - Guenther
35b - Guenther
36a - Guenther
36b - Guenther
37 - Guenther
38a - Johnson
38b - Legac
39a - Guenther
39b - Guenther
40a - Guenther
40b - Guenther
41 - Guenther
42a - Guenther
42b - Guenther
43 - Grobler
44a - Gruss
44b - Santos
45 - Pixietoe
46a - SOF
46b - Guenther
47 - Guenther
48a - SOF
48b - Tomohisa
49 - Tomohisa
50a - Guenther
50b - Santos
51 - Guenther
52a - Guenther
52b - Pixietoe
53 - Hunt
54a - Guenther
54b - Guenther
55 - Legac
56a - Esbensen
56b - Esbensen
57a - Guenther
57b - Santos
58a - Handoyo
58b - SOF
59 - SOF
60a - Santos
60b - Santos
61 - Guenther
62 - Forscek
63a - Guenther
63b - Hunt
64a - Santos
64b - Santos
65 - Guenther
66a - Santos
66b - Santos
67a - Guenther
67b - Guenther
68a - IPA
68b - Santos
69 - Gruss
70a - Gruss
70b - Gruss
71a - Guenther
71b - Santos
72 - Santos
73a - Santos
73b - Bytomski
74 - Lin
75a - Guenther
75b - SOF
76 - IPA
77 - IPA
82 - Allikas
83 - Allikas
84a - Lacerda
84b - Guenther
84c - Guenther
84d - Guenther
84e - Hunt
84f - Gruss
84g - Guenther
84h - Guenther
85a - Guenther
85b - IPA
85c - Santos
90 - Pizzol

Original Ink drawing by Kamel of *P. aphrodite* - held in the Sloan library at the British Museum of Natural History, London.

The IPA was formed in 1990 to promote the appreciation, cultivation and conservation of *Phalaenopsis* orchids.

The IPA's mission is to:

Publish the *Phalaenopsis Journal*, a quarterly magazine featuring color photography that includes articles on new lines of breeding, cultural techniques and other subjects of interest to *Phalaenopsis* growers.

Stage annual symposiums held at various locations around the world. These are filled with workshops and lectures from the foremost *Phalaenopsis* growers and hybridizers.

Bring together growers worldwide to share and to promote our passion for *Phalaenopsis* orchids.

Host PHALS Digest, an online e-mail discussion forum for our members to communicate about *Phalaenopsis* and orchid growing.

Maintain a Business Directory of IPA Members.

Provide conservancy funds to assist in the support of *Phalaenopsis* species collection maintained at the Atlanta Botanical Gardens.

Sponsor *Phalaenopsis* related projects such as *Phalaenopsis* the Genus in Pictures.

Additional copies of *Phalaenopsis* the Genus in Pictures can be ordered on the IPA website: www. phal.org.

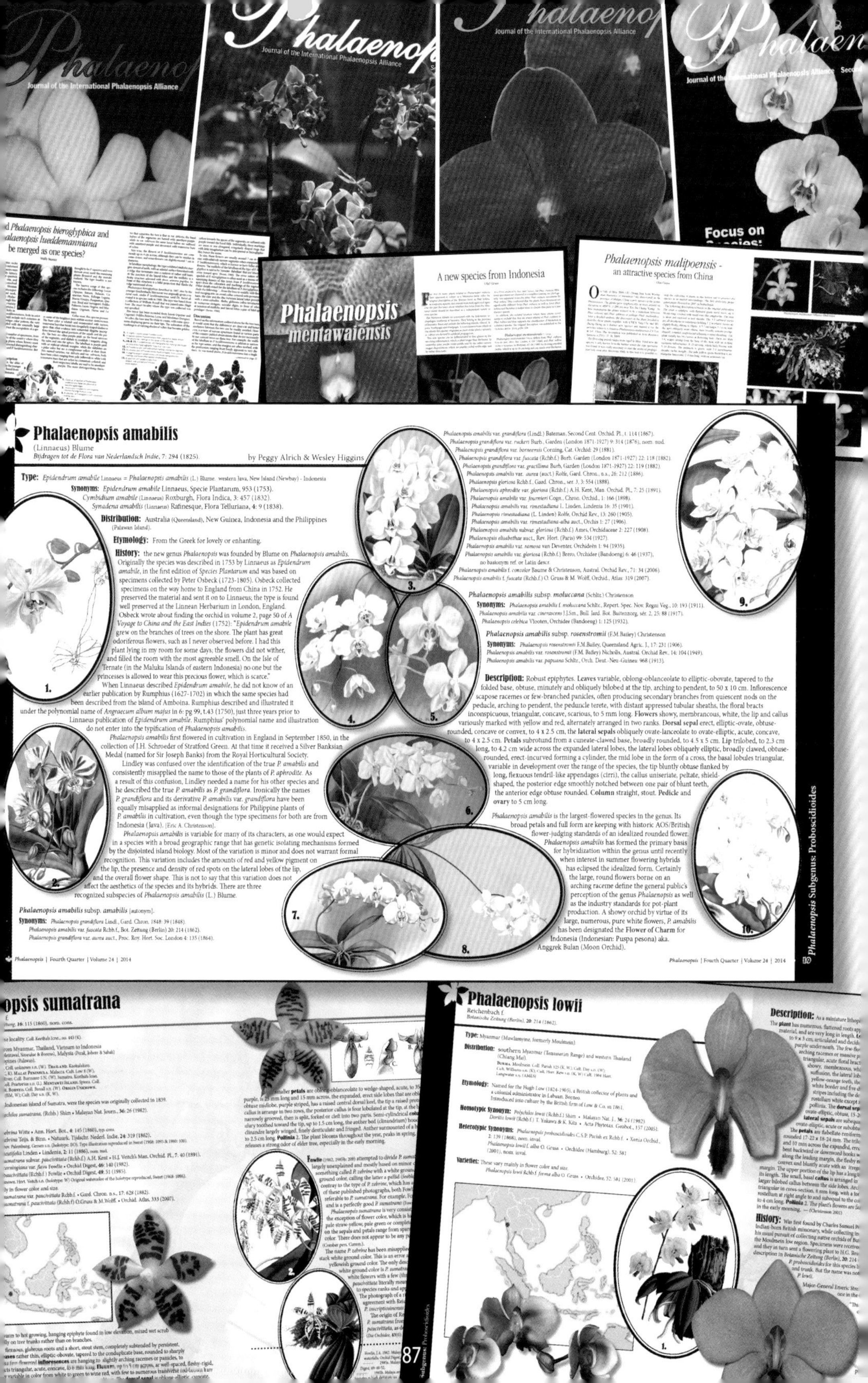

Phalaenopsis amabilis

(Linnaeus) Blume
Bijdragen tot de Flora van Nederlandsch Indie, 7: 294 (1825).

by Peggy Alrich & Wesley Higgins

Type: *Epidendrum amabile* Linnaeus = *Phalaenopsis amabilis* (L.) Blume. western Java, New Island (Newbay) - Indonesia

Synonyms: *Epidendrum amabile* Linnaeus, Specie Plantarum, 953 (1753).
Cymbidium amabile (Linnaeus) Roxburgh, Flora Indica, 3: 457 (1832).
Synadena amabilis (Linnaeus) Rafinesque, Flora Telluriana, 4: 9 (1838).

Distribution: Australia (Queensland), New Guinea, Indonesia and the Philippines (Palawan Island).

Etymology: From the Greek for lovely or enhanting.

History: the new genus *Phalaenopsis* was founded by Blume on *Phalaenopsis amabilis.* Originally the species was described in 1753 by Linnaeus as *Epidendrum amabile*, in the first edition of *Species Plantarum* and was based on specimens collected by Peter Osbeck (1723-1805). Osbeck collected specimens on the way home to England from China in 1752. He preserved the material and sent it on to Linnaeus; the type is found well preserved at the Linnean Herbarium in London, England. Osbeck wrote about finding the orchid in volume 2, page 50 of *A Voyage to China and the East Indies* (1752): "*Epidendrum amabile* grew on the branches of trees on the shore. The plant has great odoriferous flowers, such as I never observed before. I had this plant lying in my room for some days; the flowers did not wither, and filled the room with the most agreeable smell. On the Isle of Ternate (in the Maluku Islands of eastern Indonesia) no one but the princesses is allowed to wear this precious flower, which is scarce."

When Linnaeus described *Epidendrum amabile*, he did not know of an earlier publication by Rumphius (1627-1702) in which the same species had been described from the island of Amboina. Rumphius described and illustrated it under the polynomial name of *Angraecum album majus* in 6: pg 99, t.43 (1750), just three years prior to Linnaeus publication of *Epidendrum amabile*. Rumphius' polynomial name and illustration do not enter into the typification of *Phalaenopsis amabilis*.

Phalaenopsis amabilis first flowered in cultivation in England in September 1850, in the collection of J.H. Schroeder of Stratford Green. At that time it received a Silver Banksian Medal (named for Sir Joseph Banks) from the Royal Horticultural Society.

Lindley was confused over the identification of the true *P. amabilis* and consistently misapplied the name to those of the plants of *P. aphrodite*. As a result of this confusion, Lindley needed a name for his other species and he described the true *P. amabilis* as *P. grandiflora*. Ironically the names *P. grandiflora* and its derivative *P. amabilis* var. *grandiflora* have been equally misapplied as informal designations for Philippine plants of *P. amabilis* in cultivation, even though the type specimens for both are from Indonesia (Java). [Eric A. Christenson].

Phalaenopsis amabilis is variable for many of its characters, as one would expect in a species with a broad geographic range that has genetic isolating mechanisms formed by the disjointed island biology. Most of the variation is minor and does not warrant formal recognition. This variation includes the amounts of red and yellow pigment on the lip, the presence and density of red spots on the lateral lobes of the lip, and the overall flower shape. This is not to say that this variation does not affect the aesthetics of the species and its hybrids. There are three recognized subspecies of *Phalaenopsis amabilis* (L.) Blume.

Phalaenopsis amabilis* subsp. *amabilis [autonym].

Synonyms: *Phalaenopsis grandiflora* Lindl., Gard. Chron. 1848: 39 (1848).
Phalaenopsis amabilis var. *fuscata* Rchb.f., Bot. Zeitung (Berlin) 20: 214 (1862).
Phalaenopsis grandiflora var. *aurea* auct., Proc. Roy. Hort. Soc. London 4: 135 (1864).
Phalaenopsis amabilis var. *grandiflora* (Lindl.) Bateman, Second Cent. Orchid. Pl., t. 114 (1867).
Phalaenopsis grandiflora var. *ruckeri* Burb., Garden (London 1871-1927) 9: 314 (1876), nom. nud.
Phalaenopsis grandiflora var. *borneensis* Corning, Cat. Orchid: 29 (1881).
Phalaenopsis grandiflora var. *fuscata* (Rchb.f.) Burb. Garden (London 1871-1927) 22: 118 (1882).
Phalaenopsis grandiflora var. *gracillima* Burb, Garden (London 1871-1927) 22: 119 (1882).
Phalaenopsis amabilis var. *aurea* (auct.) Rolfe, Gard. Chron., n.s., 26: 212 (1886).
Phalaenopsis gloriosa Rchb.f., Gard. Chron., ser. 3, 3: 554 (1888).
Phalaenopsis aphrodite var. *gloriosa* (Rchb.f.) A.H. Kent, Man. Orchid. Pl., 7: 25 (1891).
Phalaenopsis amabilis var. *fournieri* Cogn., Chron. Orchid., 1: 166 (1898).
Phalaenopsis amabilis var. *rimestadiana* L. Linden, Lindenia 16: 35 (1901).
Phalaenopsis rimestadiana (L. Linden) Rolfe, Orchid Rev., 13: 260 (1905).
Phalaenopsis amabilis var. *rimestadiana-alba* auct., Orchis 1: 27 (1906).
Phalaenopsis amabilis subvar. *gloriosa* (Rchb.f.) Ames, Orchidaceae 2: 227 (1908).
Phalaenopsis elisabethae auct., Rev. Hort. (Paris) 99: 534 (1927).
Phalaenopsis amabilis var. *ramosa* van Deventer, Orchideèn 1: 94 (1935).
Phalaenopsis amabilis var. *gloriosa* (Rchb.f.) Brero, Orchidee (Bandoeng) 6: 46 (1937), no bastonym ref. or Latin descr.
Phalaenopsis amabilis f. *concolor* Baume & Christenson, Austral. Orchid Rev., 71: 34 (2006).
Phalaenopsis amabilis f. *fuscata* (Rchb.f.) O. Gruss & M. Wolff, Orchid., Atlas: 319 (2007).

Phalaenopsis amabilis* subsp. *moluccana (Schltr.) Christenson

Synonyms: *Phalaenopsis amabilis* f. *moluccana* Schltr., Repert. Spec. Nov. Regni Veg., 10: 193 (1911).
Phalaenopsis amabilis var. *cinerascens* J.J.Sm., Bull. Jard. Bot. Buitenzorg, sér. 2, 25: 88 (1917).
Phalaenopsis celebica Vlooten, Orchidee (Bandoeng) 1: 125 (1932).

Phalaenopsis amabilis* subsp. *rosenstromii (F.M.Bailey) Christenson

Synonyms: *Phalaenopsis rosenstromii* F.M.Bailey, Queensland Agric. J., 17: 231 (1906).
Phalaenopsis amabilis var. *rosenstromii* (F.M. Bailey) Nicholls, Austral. Orchid Rev., 14: 104 (1949).
Phalaenopsis amabilis var. *papuana* Schltr., Orch. Deut.-Neu-Guinea: 968 (1913).

Description: Robust epiphytes. **Leaves** variable, oblong-oblanceolate to elliptic-obovate, tapered to the folded base, obtuse, minutely and obliquely bilobed at the tip, arching to pendent, to 50 x 10 cm. Inflorescence scapose racemes or few-branched panicles, often producing secondary branches from quiescent nods on the peducle, arching to pendent, the peduncle terete, with distant appressed tubular sheaths, the floral bracts inconspicuous, triangular, concave, scarious, to 5 mm long. **Flowers** showy, membrancous, white, the lip and callus variously marked with yellow and red, alternately arranged in two ranks. **Dorsal sepal** erect, elliptic-ovate, obtuse-rounded, concave or convex, to 4 x 2.5 cm, the **lateral sepals** obliquely ovate-lanceolate to ovate-elliptic, acute, concave, to 4 x 2.5 cm. **Petals** subrotund from a cuneate-clawed base, broadly rounded, to 4.5 x 5 cm. **Lip** trilobed, to 2.3 cm long, to 4.2 cm wide across the expanded lateral lobes, the lateral lobes obliquely elliptic, broadly clawed, obtuse-rounded, erect-incurved forming a cylinder, the mid lobe in the form of a cross, the basal lobules triangular, variable in development over the range of the species, the tip bluntly obtuse flanked by long, flexuous tendril-like appendages (cirri), the callus uniseriate, peltate, shield-shaped, the posterior edge smoothly notched between one pair of blunt teeth, the anterior edge obtuse rounded. **Column** straight, stout. **Pedicle** and **ovary** to 5 cm long.

Phalaenopsis amabilis is the largest-flowered species in the genus. Its broad petals and full form are keeping with historic AOS/British flower-judging standards of an idealized rounded flower. *Phalaenopsis amabilis* has formed the primary basis for hybridization within the genus until recently when interest in summer flowering hybrids has eclipsed the idealized form. Certainly the large, round flowers borne on an arching raceme define the general public's perception of the genus *Phalaenopsis* as well as the industry standards for pot-plant production. A showy orchid by virtue of its large, numerous, pure white flowers, *P. amabilis* has been designated the **Flower of Charm** for Indonesia (Indonesian: Puspa pesona) aka. Anggrek Bulan (Moon Orchid).

Phalaenopsis lowii, The Garden (London) **9**: 14 (1876).